ep;phany
a literary journal

Publisher	Willard Cook
Editor	Odette Heideman
Poetry Editor	Nick Admussen
Editor at Large	Joel Hinman
Contributing Editors	Martin Edmunds, Karol Nielsen, Martin Rock Christopher Shade
Interviews Editor	Adrienne Brock
Readers	Jasper Creegan, John Greenberg Susan Hendel, Susie Marples
CoverDesign	Gabe Cook
Friends of Epiphany	Bernie & Elsie Aidinoff, Sallie Bingham Vicky Bjur Literary Agency, Augustus Crocker The Cook Family Fund, Heleny Cook & Richard Hall, Paul & Marcia Cook Rebecca J. Cook, Warrren & Brammie Cook Lavinia Currier, Lisa Dierbeck, Dawn & Andy Eig, Martin Edmunds, Elizabeth England George Franklin, Yoko Fukuda, Haruko Fukuda Eiko Fukuda, Irene Goodale, Michele Herman Edward Hirsch, Etgar Keret, Remy Kothe Jefferey Lependorf, Sarah Lutz, Elizabeth Macklin Heather MacMaster, Jerry & Naomi Neuwirth Edith Pearlman, Monica Racic, Roxanna Robinson Pierre George Roy, Vicki Scher, Phillip Schultz Richard Smolev, Ken & Michelle Stiller John van Rens, Derek Walcott John Edgar Wideman
Board of Directors	Willard Cook, Lisa Dierbeck, Elizabeth England Lisa Kaufman, Remy Kothe, Lisa Paolella

Epiphany is published biannually by Epiphany Magazine, Inc., a nonprofit §401(c)(3) corporation.

For submission guidelines, please visit our Web site at epiphanyzine.com

Donations and gifts to *Epiphany* are tax-deductible to the extent allowed by law.

A one-year subscription is $20; a two-year subscription is $38. Make checks payable to Epiphany Magazine and send to: 71 Bedford Street, New York, NY 10014 or visit our website at epiphanyzine.com

The ISBN number is 0-9749047-5-9   The ISSN number is 1937-9811

THE WINTER 2014 ISSUE WAS PRINTED BY:
THE SHERIDAN PRESS 450 FAME AVENUE HANOVER, PA 17331

MISSION STATEMENT: *Epiphany* is committed to publishing literary work, wherever it may fall on the spectrum from experimental to traditional, that is realized both in its vision and in its devotion to artistry. We are especially open to writers whose explorations of new territory may not yet have found validation elsewhere.

Bookstore distribution is through Ingram Periodicals (ingramperiodicals.com) and Ubiquity Distributors (ubiquitymags.com).

Epiphany is a member of the Council of Literary Magazines & Presses.

SFI
Certified Sourcing
www.sfiprogram.org
SFI-01075

CONTENTS

[FICTION]

[GRAPHICS]

[MEMOIR]

[NONFICTION]

[POEMS]

Amorak Huey

SELF-PORTRAIT AS DUSTIN HOFFMAN IN "TOOTSIE"

Divorce unshapes our family into a set of occasionally
intersecting lines. It means more movies, more swearing,
more time in cars. Transitions are shaped like doorknobs.
For the first time, hours are countable. I learn early the
importance of ritual and mask, the way silence falls from
the light slicing through the darkness over our heads,
a wedge widening until it reaches the blank screen and
becomes someone else's adventure story. I am too young for
any of this. The world isn't waiting for me to be the right
age. I whisper profanity but no one hears me. I speak with
a New York accent for the entire year I am twelve. I am
waiting for my life to include an apartment, a roommate,
a party on the roof of a building made of glass and sex and
alcohol. Maybe cigarettes. I will wear whatever you ask
me to, but it never was about the shimmering dress, the
eyeliner, the foundation. It was always about Jessica Lange's
mouth and how the life you deserve is worth lying for.

Chun Sue

DREAMING OF LIVING
INSIDE A DREAM

(translated by Martin Winter)

taking pictures by day
then sleepless at night
in a dream, making love to a foe
making love to a spy
making same-sex love
making love to the one who caressed me
making love to the one who harassed me
in a dream, won't be no fire
won't be no great snow
in a dream, making love, shoot to kill
panicking, heart-broken
showing colorful clothes
holding in gushing feelings
or gushing blood

Tia Clark

LIKE REAL WOMEN

Ray wants to see Caramel's insides, so before he heads out east, he stops at Foxies Gentleman's Club. He still remembers her first night of work: her slow walk down to the main stage, and how those smaller stages around it with the blondes, brunettes, and redheads dancing their familiar flat-bellied wiggle seemed to disappear. It was as if the tight white skin wrapped around their small bones didn't look the same kind of pinchable that it did the day before. The day before, he'd liked those dancers fine; the way their eyes looked when they pushed their small breasts together and thanked him for the single dollar he slipped in the cleavage.

But Caramel's first dance, her sway to a dreamy beat and tight grip to her own thick thighs, made Ray forget to swallow. Made his neck sweat. She worked the edge of the stage, stopping in front of each man to give dance enough to warrant a dollar in her waistband. When she got to Ray, she crouched slow and tugged at the bikini string by her neck that kept her breasts hidden from him. She pulled hard once and it fell, her breasts round and hanging down low toward her belly. She turned away from Ray and dropped to all fours to crawl to the next man. She was bent over enough so Ray could see the shape of her through her G-string. Foxies was topless only. Ray knew that was the best he could get.

Offstage, Caramel whispered a lap-dance offer in each man's ear. Ray accepted. She held on to his hand with hers, and he watched her bare and loose midsection jiggle when her hips switched.

She sat him down in an empty seat in the dark back room of fold-out chairs. He'd never been to the back before. Always thought lap dances were ripoffs. When the song started, she rolled her body over him with black, forward eyes. It was already worth it. He looked into them, and felt hot, but she broke into a big smile and laughed.

"Relax," she said. "Just watch me."

Was he not relaxed? He shifted around in his seat and tried to slack his shoulders. She smiled still, showing the wide space between her two front teeth.

"That's a nice shirt," she said, and touched his nipple with her nail. He flinched and pulled his body inward. There were things he wanted to say to her, but with her so close, he couldn't get to them. He felt like his teenage self, before he learned how to grab a breast. But there she stood with hers in his face. He wanted her nipple in his mouth. She brushed his cheek with it.

She straddled him and leaned back, and where their laps met, he could see the outline of her again. "Do you wanna see in here?" she asked, pointing at the spot. He nodded.

She came back up and smiled. The song ended. "One song per customer," she said. "I guess you'll have to come back." She licked her bottom lip and smiled. He wanted to punch her and kiss her.

At home, Ray searched for Caramels in rap videos, in Ebony porn, by Googling "hot black chicks." None of them had her smile, her skin, her ass, her voice. He wanted to grab her by her waist-length hair and pull. He wanted to watch her face twist up, her mouth open, the space between her teeth. He looked at the objects around his apartment, wondering what he could fit into her gap. A matchbook? The side of a quarter? The blunt tip of a butter knife? He wanted her to think he could split her open.

So, he went the next night to try again. It was less crowded than the last night, and this night, Caramel stood by the door.

"Well well well," she said to Ray. "You back to see my pussy?" She smiled at him.

He bought another dance from her, and stared at her breasts and her sex near his eyes and mouth. "You wanna see it?" she asked.

He nodded. She slid her G-string to the side with her two longest fingers and exposed herself.

The lighting in the back room was as dark as it was on the stage and Ray could barely make out the shape of her. He thought about flicking a lighter near so he could see better. But she continued her dance. Afterwards, he bought her a tequila sunrise.

He kept buying dances, and over the course of a month, they got close. They'd chat at the bar, and sometimes when it was dead Ray would put in a Chinese food order with the girls. Caramel told him she came out to Kansas with a military man, but when they broke up, she picked up stripping to maintain. He told her sparse details about his ex-wife and Michelle. How he missed being a dad and how he sometimes thought about trying to contact her, but how hard it would be after so long. Caramel rubbed his shoulders. She gave him private dances in the dark, and he never got around to saying he wanted to see inside of her for real. He didn't know how you say something like that.

She didn't like him, because he was too old and too white, he figured. Too nice and nervous. He bought too many drinks and dances for her to respect him as anything other than a customer.

He claimed it was coincidental that he decided to take a job out east after Caramel mentioned that she was quitting Foxies. There was a cosmetology school down the road from the club, and she'd saved just enough for it. Ray's one-bedroom basement apartment and job at the leather factory weren't worth staying for on their own. He'd never been out of the Midwest, but he knew the East Coast moved faster. Caramel told him all about her New York City nightlife, and Elmsford, the square-mile town she grew up in. She said the little town buzzed louder than Kansas. She planned to go back eventually, and maybe she'd see him out there on a side street somewhere. She'd look him up when she got in the area, she promised.

So now, with his truck packed up, Ray pulls into the Foxies parking lot to say goodbye. He prefers it like this, in the daytime when there are fewer men around. Today there's only one, but there are girls. Long hair and short, all twiggy and smiling. It's too dark to see into their eyes, really, and Ray prefers the distance. He likes the other girls to be anonymous. They know him, though, and a few of them wish him luck on his journey. He avoids their eyes; they look like his ex-wife when she was thinner, or his daughter when she gets older, his pale-skinned neighbor, a cousin, etc. They look like real women.

Caramel comes out from the back in a tight pink dress and puts her arms around Ray. She takes his hand and leads him to the V.I.P. section.

He puts a twenty in her V-neck right away.

"So this is the end." Her whisper still gets him like the first time. She never says anything about the hard-ons.

"This is it," he says. She starts to dance, but soon puts her arm around his neck and her head to his shoulder. It's less like a lover and more like a child.

"You were my favorite," she says.

Come away with me, he thinks. I'll take you back home. Or we can start a new home out there. I'll put a spotlight by our bed. "There's room in my truck," he says.

She laughs and hits his chest. She grinds her hips on him. It's slow and sensual. She breathes on his neck.

Let's turn on the lights. Let me see how you really look. Let me see.

She stands up and pulls her panties to the side again, showing him darkness.

"I can't see." Ray reaches out and touches it, just like that. She flinches, but looks at him in the eyes. It gets brighter or he focuses, and he realizes that her real name probably isn't Caramel.

They're frozen there, and he slides the finger inside her. The second feels like a warm minute. She grabs his hand and pulls it out.

"No," she says. "You can't do that." She closes her eyes and continues to dance. A little faster. Like she's rushing. When it's done, she kisses him on the cheek. "Take care," she says, and walks back out toward the stage.

R ay is three days out of Kansas when he sees the FOOD, GAS, AND SERVICE sign at the Elmsford exit. He's been holding his piss since New Jersey. He parks his F-150 by the first gas pump at the Sunoco.

It isn't too out of his way to stop here and see the streets that Caramel used to walk, where she went to school, if anyone in town looked like her. He'll just drive around the roads a few times, he figures, maybe stop at a strip club for old time's sake, if he can find one. He's tired, and considering getting a room with a bed for the night. And he can't shake Caramel's face when she walked away. It was maybe pain, maybe fear, maybe disinterest. He wants to make it up to her, how he got carried away because it was her and because it was the end, and because maybe it was something like love. He'll try again in Elmsford. Some woman somewhere in this town could use a guy like Ray.

He's got no patience to look for a toilet. Instead, he walks toward the side of the Minimart in his worn-out work boots. On his way, he sees some teenage Spanish boys huddled in the corner by a Paul Bunyan statue that's missing both arms. A couple of young blacks in big sweat-shirts with brown bags are in their own huddle by the door.

He slides down his zipper and pulls out through the opening. The walls of the gas station are graffiti-stained and filthy. He wonders if Caramel ever bought potato chips and pop here.

He hears a faint noise coming from the back of the Sunoco. He shifts weight from heels to toes and back again. Then he hears *shhh*. A *shhh* of bad behavior.

He creeps around the building with his back toward the road and peeks around the corner of it. Two little girls in tiny black dresses and yellow-brown Spanish skin huddle together and shiver from the mid-October air. They don't see him as they whisper.

"What are ya'll doin' back here?" he asks. They jump, the both of them, and their doe-like faces look jacked by headlights. One drops a liquor bottle from her hands and glass shatters into pieces on the gravel, letting clear liquid flow down the slight decline. They band together, their arms sealed tight where they meet. Ray takes a good look at them. They're like twins; they stand no taller than five feet, similar complexion, small, new breasts, same eye makeup, short black dresses. One has long, straight hair and the other has wet-looking curls at her shoulder.

"I didn't mean to scare you," he says. They don't move, except the shaking from the cold, or from fear, and Ray remembers himself: a man in his forties with unwashed hands, a graying beard he hasn't shaved in days, stains on the dark-green shirt peeking from his Carhartt, stains on his Levi's, smelling like the road. Facing two pubescent girls in too-tight dresses with a puddle of vodka running between them. He thinks fast.

"I was wondering if ya'll could tell me where there's a McDonalds around here." He chuckles to lighten the mood. "Relax, I'm not police or anything."

The one with the straight hair speaks up. "There's no McDonalds except in White Plains, but we got Wendy's, KFC, Taco Bell, Burger King."

"All right, all right, I'll take anything, whatever's closest."

The one with the wavy hair tells Ray about the KFC drive-through down the road past the first light.

"Thank you. Y'all be careful." He nods and turns back.

The two of them out there like that, so small, he could scoop them up in one arm if he wanted to. They're only twenty miles up from New York City in this little town, with dark alleyways and homeless men. One could come around a corner and jerk it to their kid faces. Those black guys in front of the Minimart with the brown bags. One scoop, he thinks, they could be gone in one scoop.

"Hey, I'm real sorry about your bottle, I didn't mean to scare ya." He sees them tense. "But I gotta know, what are you girls doin' out here in this cold? You got no coats on, it's damn near eleven at night, you're drunk—"

"We're not drunk," the curly-haired one snaps.

"All right, but you're drinkin'. Now, I'm a father. And I know I'd be damned if my daughter was out here and nobody said a good word to her." And if these girls aren't careful, they'll end up dancing for dirty old men one day. The wavy-haired one pops her gum.

"So what?" she says. "You're not our dad."

"That's right, I'm not. Are you girls waiting for someone? Someone's comin' to pick you up?"

The one with the straight hair stays silent as the bold one speaks. "We're goin' to White Plains," she says.

"For what?" Ray remembers White Plains from a few exits back. He remembers tall buildings. Bright city lights.

"None of your business," she says. "But if you must know, we're going to a party."

"Do you need a ride?" he asks. The wavy-haired one rolls her eyes. "Listen, I'm not trying to cause any trouble. Like I said, I'm a father. I feel funny leavin' you out here like this."

"Can you replace our bottle since you made us drop it?" the bold one says.

"Deal," Ray says, and regrets it. Perhaps this is too far. He knows nothing about the cops around here. Nothing about these girls. Not how much they drank, or how much such tiny bodies can handle. But he knows how they look, and he knows men. He knows if he doesn't get them liquor, another man will. It could be a bigger man, more tired, driving from further out west. If any girl needs more saving than them, Ray doubts he'll find her anytime soon.

"Deal," she says.

"No," says the long-haired one. "Jonessa, let's just go."

"Yeah, says the girl who broke my damn bottle."

"O.K., Jonessa, what's more important, your bottle or your goddam life?" She lowers her voice, but Ray can still hear. "We don't know this man. I'm not trying to get us raped and killed by some stranger. Let's just go."

This is how he imagines Michelle: a girl with a good head on her shoulders. She probably drinks beer and smokes pot, but he can live with that if she stays out of strangers' cars. He shifts his weight heel to toe and looks beyond the girls to the highway. He could hop right back on it and get out of this town with no traces.

"It's all right," he says. "I get it. Just promise me you girls will be safe. I better get going anyway."

"Wait," Jonessa says. "We'll take the ride. And the bottle."

So Ray walks the girls from the back of the Sunoco to where he left his truck. "It's a climb," he apologizes. He takes Jonessa's hand to help her up. When the other one goes in, she shoos his hand away and hops. He shuts their door.

As he fills his gas tank, he watches them through the window. They're mad at each other. Then they're giggling. Then Jonessa looks at Ray like, What are you lookin' at? He turns his head away and looks at the few stars.

He hangs the pump and climbs in the truck beside them.

"So," he says, shutting the door. "Where to? How can I help?" They share one seat but they fit fine in the front, so tiny and bare-legged, with knees smaller than his fist.

"There's a liquor store right up the street," Jonessa says. She'd crossed her legs left over right and leaned her body into her friend as if to avoid touching Ray. They smell like flowers and bubble baths. Like scented lotion. Like candle wax. Like vodka.

"So what are your names?" Ray asks.

"I'm Jonessa," Jonessa says, putting a palm to her chest. "This is Linda."

"What's your name?" Linda asks.

"Ray McKinney. I'm from way out in Ogden, Kansas."

"Sheesh, she didn't ask for your damn life story," Jonessa says, looking out the passenger window. Her voice makes everything seem like a bite.

"Who's that?" Linda asks, grazing her fingers over the baby picture on the dashboard.

"That's my daughter Michelle."

"She's pretty," Linda says. "How old is she?"

"Oh, she's about your age."

"Damn, I feel bad for her," Linda says. "I bet you don't let her do nothing. You're probably, like, the world's strictest dad." He doesn't want to look directly at the girls, but from the corner of his eye he can see Linda smiling and looking his way.

"No, she doesn't live with me. Her mother..." He pauses. "Her mother handles all that stuff." The car is quiet for a block. "So what do you do for fun out here? What's it like for a kid growing up in these parts?"

"Lame," Jonessa says. "Really lame. Why do you think we go to White Plains? That's where everything fun is. Out here is just a bunch of blacks and Mexicans doing stupid shit."

"So people try to move out of here a lot? People run away?"

"Hell, yeah, wouldn't you? I'm getting my ass out of here no matter what," Jonessa says. She's looking out the window. "Stop!" she says. She points to Elmsford Wine and Spirits on the right, lit and glowing. Ray pulls into the parking lot.

"O.K., get us..." Jonessa bites her bottom lip and rolls her eyes up in thought. "Patrón. The medium bottle of Patrón."

Ray snickers. "You were drinkin' vodka. Cheap vodka."

"I like a man who knows his liquor." Bite. Ray can't tell how drunk she is. He's confused about a child's ability to hold her liquor. How do they learn such a skill?

"How about a small bottle of Smirnoff," he insists.

"Wait, what flavor?" Jonessa asks.

"White grape," Linda says.

"Yuck. White grape makes me freakin' gag."

"Fine, regular then."

"Wow, alcoholic, you want me to chug regular vodka?"

Chug? Ray thinks.

"Jonessa, you're being fucking difficult. What flavor do you want?" Linda says. Linda's a little darker than Jonessa and she still has a sweetness to her. Where Jonessa bites, Linda nibbles.

"Just surprise us," Jonessa says. Ray takes his keys out of the ignition to be safe. These girls are smart in that sort of way, he can tell.

He walks into the liquor palace. The colored drinks shine through the freezer glass like Christmas lights, and he can taste the brown ones on sight. Ray grabs a Raspberry Smirnoff and fights himself for a minute before getting a small bottle of Buffalo Trace.

The girl at the checkout counter has long dry braids that fall over the front of her shoulders. Her skin is as black as Caramel's nipples. Her name tag says "Kerani." Her mouth is plump and glossy. Ray touches his neck with his fingers and imagines they're her lips.

Kerani breaks the part in her hair by running her hand through the middle. He thinks of pulling her braids out one by one and her enjoying it.

"How you doin' today?" she says mechanically. She slides the first bottle across the scanner.

"Just fine, ma'am," he says. She looks up. Her eyebrows scrunch and she smiles.

"'Ma'am'?" she says. "Wow. You must just be driving through." He wants to ask how old she is so he can feel O.K. imagining how she tastes. Based on her smell, he imagines strawberry ice cream melting down her chest. He licks his lips before it drips down. He swallows.

"I'm out here from Kansas," he says. She takes a braid on the left side and twirls it around her finger. He nods, and she taps a few touch-screen buttons with the pink plastic nails on her other hand.

"Kansas, huh? That's way out there," she says. When she smiles, he can see all her teeth, fangs and fillings, a twisted one on the far right. He notes the darkness of her wide gum. He sees a gap in the front two. It's nothing like Caramel's, much tighter. But still.

"Yes, ma'am," Ray says. "Say, you got any family out in Kansas?"

She shakes her head and the braids sway. "Why, I look like somebody?" With the same hand, she swoops every braid to one side. Ray remembers his Sunoco. Just that it's down there.

"Yeah, you do, actually. Just like this young lady I know," he says. "She's actually from here."

"From Elmsford? Nobody's from here," Kerani says. "I probably know her. What's her name?"

If Ray knew her real name, he would tell Kerani. He just smiles. "I'm gonna respect her privacy on this one."

Kerani, with her big batty eyes, puts her tongue between her teeth and smiles. "How respectful. Well, if she looks like me, she must be beautiful," she says.

"Stunning." He has a million questions. Mainly, What time do you get off? Can I please see you? How old are you?

She tells him the total and he passes over his credit card. When she takes it, their hands touch, as though she could grab his and take him to the back of the store and show him. But maybe when he goes to pull those braids out, she'll stare ahead and tell him "no."

He looks out to his truck and sees the girls shaking their heads, and Jonessa crossing her arms over her chest. Ray chokes down the excess spit that formed in his mouth. He wishes Kerani a good night. He takes the brown bag and walks out the belled Push door with a pain in his crotch.

In the car, Jonessa's arms are folded across her chest and she's pouting like a toddler. Linda is pushing keys on a cell phone with her thumbs.

"What happened here?" he asks, putting the bottles by his feet. "Why all the frowns?"

"The party's shut down," Linda says. "Cops busted it up for under-age drinking."

"That's what you kids around here are all about, huh?" Ray says.

"You don't understand," Jonessa says.

"It's just a party," Ray says, looking over. "You got years of parties to go to, if you ask me."

"You don't get it," she says again. "And I didn't ask you."

"It's at her boyfriend's house," Linda says. "And he's on probation, so this could ruin his life." He didn't imagine them with boyfriends. It makes sense that Jonessa, all pouty and tough, has one. But he hopes Linda doesn't. He hopes Michelle doesn't. He hopes no men come around the good girls.

"Probation? How old is this guy?"

"Fuck you, none of your business." Jonessa's eyes moisten at the corners and Ray almost wants to laugh. Years from now, she'll dance on some man's stage and forget Ray even exists.

"I'm just gonna take you girls home, then," he says. "This is getting a little out of hand."

"No!" The simultaneous scream shocks him. Their eyes become children's.

"Jonessa told her parents that she was sleeping at my place, and I told my mom I was sleeping at her place," Linda says. Jonessa puts her fingertips at her temples and rubs, staring down at the floor of Ray's truck.

"This is bad. This is bad. This is bad. Fuck. Move," Jonessa says to Linda. She climbs over her friend's lap and grabs the door. She unlocks it and gets out.

"Where is she going?" Ray asks. It's all fast now. The cars are speeding.

Linda looks out the door around the truck. "She's just sobering up."

"Sobering up?"

"Yeah, she's puking." Linda's voice is calm still.

"I didn't know she was so drunk," he says. "She didn't look sick."

"I don't think she's sick. She's just throwing up." Linda climbs out of the truck, too, and Ray sits for a moment. The lights are on in the liquor store. This could be another man's problem. He hears her dry heave.

He gets out of the truck and walks around the front to get to their side. Jonessa is on all fours. He sees the bottom of her underwear and tries to avert his eyes. Linda has her arm on Jonessa's back, and Jonessa has her longest finger reaching in her throat, gagging, spitting out attempts at vomit.

"Wait a minute," Ray says. "You feelin' sick?" He walks to the front of them. Jonessa looks up at him with big eyes, her fingers still by her mouth, waiting. Ray can't tell how old she is anymore. She looks too much like a woman for him to know what a father would say.

"I can't go home like this," she says. "My dad." She closes her eyes tight. "At least let me get it all out. He'll know." Her voice quivers more than Ray thought it could.

He looks at the passing cars on the road. These are another man's kids. But none of the cars slow down. There's no man around to claim them. This is his to take care of.

"Don't cry," Ray says. "You don't have to go home. We'll figure something out." Linda looks up at Ray, and then down to Jonessa for an answer. Jonessa has stopped trying to puke. Her arm rests limply by her body and she lets herself come off of her knees and sit with her bottom on the floor against Ray's truck. Linda takes a seat next to her on the concrete. Ray looks at them resting on his car with their small bodies in small dresses. "What do you girls wanna do?" he asks. The lights from the liquor store shine over them, putting them in clear view. "Let's get back in the car. We'll figure it out." Their eyes look up to him, saying O.K., saying Let's go, saying Yes. ◆

Leora Fridman

PITY ISN'T WHAT I HAVE
IN MY HANDS

I am some grounded
religion

I am some answer
no one spelled

meaning also
I make a living

I explain
the best caress

like what obvious metals
does the earth most need

and which ones
can we leave

praying
for ourselves

Aaron DeLee

SELFIE: BLOODY MARY

Who did you expect to find in this frame?
              Lowering the lights blackens all from view;
Bloody Mary, Candy Man, I'm just the same

shade hidden, playing a perilous game
              that all indestructible children do.
Who did you expect to find in this frame

when slowly chanting rosaries of name
              and curse, whispered as if knelt in the pew:
Bloody Mary, Candy Man. I'm just the same

as I was when eight, gripped with monsters; Fame,
              some pop star called it. The mirror is true—
Who did you expect to find in this frame?

It's a Thanatos complex; pour acclaim
              and sate my thirst, I covet the ooh and boo.
Bloody Mary, Candy Man, I'm just the same,

a ghoul waiting to break through. You're to blame
              when hands clap like lights flicked on. I am you.
Who did you expect to find in this frame?
              Bloody Mary, Candy Man, I'm just the same.

Alexander Maksik

AT THE SEAWALL

The beach was full of glistening people spread out on towels and on chairs beneath umbrellas and there was the smell of meat being cooked and everywhere, it seemed, everywhere there was something to eat.

She walked down to the edge of the sea and splashed water on her face and over the back of her neck. She drew herself up and turned and walked with as much confidence as she could muster. At the seawall, she climbed the stairs and went to a bench, where she sat and adjusted her expression and set herself to appear purposeful and at peace. She crossed her right knee over her left and when the skirt drew up to reveal her legs, she left the skin exposed. She raised her chin and extended her arms out across the back of the bench, a posture, it seemed to her, of ease and openness. As if she might be thinking about the beauty of that strange dark-blue sea, or waiting for a lover, or for her children and her husband.

Now the sun was low and the wind had come up. The sunbathers returned their sunscreen and magazines and books to their bags. They pulled on their shirts and dresses and hats. A thin girl leaned over so that her long light hair hung free. She sprayed it with something from a bottle and then pulled a brush through over and over. Between the brushstrokes, the sunlight came and went, came and went.

Jacqueline waited, leaning back, with her arms still spread out behind her—a young woman come to sit and watch the sunset. Two policemen walked along the sidewalk. She felt sick again and concentrated on the mast of a sailboat gliding around the point from the direction of her cave.

They didn't stop and when she saw their backs, and could no longer hear them speaking, she returned her foot to the ground and leaned forward with her elbows on her knees, chin in her hands.

The beach was emptying and she was strong enough to stand and return to the sand, but now there were sturdy, handsome men coming out to stack the chairs and clear the trash. They took their time as the sun continued to fall, stopping to talk to one another, scooping up half-empty bottles of water. They collected grease-stained paper bags and soda cans, both of which appeared heavy in their hands. Nothing looked empty to her, and the slowness of the men made her angry. She could not wait any longer. She stood up too fast and steadied herself on the railing. When the world came back to center, she prepared to walk.

It would be a stroll along the shoreline. She would be reflective. A thin woman recovering her life.

She descended the steps and walked onto the black sand, which was still very warm. All along the beach, the men were stacking the plastic chairs. She went to the edge of the sea and walked with her feet in the water. The trash bags were in piles. There was a woman and a man, an older boy chasing two young girls running figure eights in the shallow water. Jacqueline stopped and looked at the sea. There were more boats now. Sunset cruises. Music rose and fell, warped by the wind.

She did not look at the family.

Please leave.

Please go.

Please leave something. Please leave something, she thought. What she meant was, Please leave me something, but she would not say it, not even to herself. She set her eyes on a sleek speedboat tearing across the horizon, its bow rising and then falling to slap the surface of the water.

Please.

Prayer, her mother said.

She turned and they were gone and Jacqueline saw that they'd left something.

Answered.

She would not race to anything. Or from it. That was more important. She would be slow in all things.

She sat in their depressions. Then, as if it had been hers all along, she reached over and took the bottle and unscrewed the top and turned it to her lips and drank. The water was warm and as it filled her mouth and ran down her throat, she began to cry. She felt something solid pass across her tongue, a piece of bread maybe, or a bit of onion.

It was so often relief that made her cry. Not pain or disappointment or horror or terror, but instead it was relief from those things. Relief and, sometimes still, love. She drank it all, nearly half a liter. She knew to drink bit by bit, but did not, so the water hurt her throat and then there was twist of pain in her stomach, and then that sick hollowness at the top of her chest.

Patience, her mother said. And faith.

Jacqueline reached for the bag and laid it on the sand between her feet and tore it open. Inside was crumpled foil lined with white wax paper, and when she'd spread it all out, she found a piece of flatbread the size of her palm, and there were also scraps of roasted lamb. They'd been salted and rubbed with thyme leaves, and in brighter light they'd have shone. She counted the pieces of meat. Seven of them the size of her fingertips and an eighth piece as long and as thick as her little toe, which was there on the sand for comparison. She touched the bread and found the side on which the sauce had been spread. She tore it in half and collected the meat from the paper and made a sandwich, and then she ate with as much control as she could find in herself. She chewed the first bite and counted her jaw closing twenty times before she swallowed.

To be elegant, to be graceful, to be beautiful, we must do everything slowly. Nearly everything. There are some things that require us to be quick. But those things are powerful only because we do everything else slowly. One thing makes the other. Count if you're not sure.

Jacqueline counted and looked at her mother, but it was not the counting that put her on the sand, made that narrow face, those soft black eyes appear before her, made her speak, made her raise her chin, made her laugh, it was not the counting, it was the thyme.

Thyme was in her jollof. Heavy in it. Heavier than anyone's. It did not disappear behind the tomato paste, beneath the ginger. Less salt, more thyme. You roast it dry in an iron pan first with the black pepper and with chili seeds and salt. Roast it dry just until it begins to smoke and then add the oil and the onions. Then you start the rest. You do everything slowly, her mother said.

Cooking, the only domestic work her mother allowed herself.

Jacqueline's stomach twisted and cramped. Still, the pleasure. She hated the stale and acrid taste of her own mouth. It was the taste of hunger, and now it had been replaced by flavors of fat and salt, bread and thyme. It was not enough, but now she had eaten, she had had some water. Now she could get control of herself. Now she could see what was there. ◆

An Interview with Alexander Maksik

Two news headlines caught my eye as I was formulating questions for this interview: "EBOLA OUT OF CONTROL: QUARANTINES, HUNGER AND DEATH IN LIBERIA" (Reuters, 8/17/14 and "MIGRANTS WHO MAKE IT TO GREECE ARE SOON DESPERATE TO FLEE AGAIN" (International New York *Times*, 8/8/14).

When I read these articles, I immediately thought of the character in Xander Maksik's remarkable novel, *A Marker to Measure Drift*: the story of a young woman from a family of privilege who struggles as a victim of civil war. When we meet her, she has narrowly escaped from her native Liberia—a land that has devolved into a state of unimaginable savagery. Jacqueline has found her way to the island of Santorini. In this idyllic land of the carefree, the voices of her past life inhabit her thoughts as she teeters to reenter the arena of a humane society. The book is a quietly devastating exploration of the human capacity to choose; in Jacqueline's case, the choice is fundamental: to live or to die.

—Odette Heideman

◆

O. H.: *Jacqueline's desperate struggle to merely survive reminded me often of* Life and Times of Michael K., *by J. M. Coetzee. Michael, made "other" by his harelip from birth, reduces his life to barely an existence, finding pleasure in simple luxuries: the freedom resulting from his isolation; a slice of roasted homegrown pumpkin. Jacqueline clings to her dignity in a similar fashion: it attaches her to her former life as much as making a mattress out of trash does. How did you come to this character? Is she based on someone you observed or knew?*

A. M.: When I read *Life and Times of Michael K.,* I was staying with my girlfriend at her parent's house in Viols-en-Laval, a tiny village in the Hérault not far from Montpellier. We were spending a lot of time out at the beaches, and then stopping in the city on the way home. Through the course of those days I'd see so many versions of France—the variety of people on the sand, and those on the Place de la Comédie. Then we'd drive home through villages just like Viols-en-Laval and be returned to a more homogenous France, where there was often talk of "the immigrant threat." Many of the people I knew there were *pieds noirs*, so their mistrust of a rapidly changing France was deepened and complicated by their experiences in Algeria. All of this is to say that *Life and Times* was exactly the right book at exactly the right time, and when I finished it I felt, among many other things, a profound sense of relief. As if I'd been somehow granted permission to write the book I wanted to write. I think Coetzee's novel is extraordinary—its structure, its intense focus and intimacy, and most of all the combination of fury and tenderness with which it must have been written.

I began writing *A Marker to Measure Drift* a few weeks later. There were many other influences, of course, but that book was crucial. Jacqueline isn't based on anyone I've ever known, but she is certainly an amalgamation of many people I've talked with or observed throughout France and Spain, Italy and Greece. And then, of course, she possesses many of the qualities I admire in certain women I know—intelligence, strength, passion, independence, toughness, and anger.

O.H.: *The great South African writer Nadine Gordimer died this week. After being awarded the Nobel Prize in Literature, she stressed that no matter where she was born, she would have become a writer. It happened that she was born into a world where apartheid reigned. Which came first for you: the politics of Jacqueline's predicament or the character?*

A.M.: Simply and to begin with, I knew that I wanted to write about someone from somewhere else. For as long as I can remember, I've been interested in those stories, which are always, in one way or another, immigrant stories. But it wasn't until I moved to Paris that I became so sharply aware of, as you say, the politics of the predicament. I hated the way that people of African descent were treated there. It made me angry, and it entirely altered my perception of that mythic city, and of France. It changed the way I lived, where I spent my time, and ultimately it forced me to take on subjects I might never have otherwise. Really, I don't think there's any separating a character from her politics. All good novels are political. That said, in setting out to write *Marker*, I was in search of a character, not an argument. I didn't start writing to be political, but I will say that writing, both this novel and in general, has certainly made me more political.

O.H.: *Because the perspective of the narrator is so specifically focused on Jacqueline's story, the issue of racism is almost crowded out. It's as if she has wrestled this topic to the ground, controlling it with her conscious manipulation of how the world sees her. Instead,* A Marker to Measure Drift *investigates permutations of the theme: immigration, migration, and assimi-*

lation. *I imagine there was a fair amount of research that you undertook in order to write with such intimate detail. You have never been to Liberia, I have read. How did you research Jacqueline's situation? Do you follow immigration issues—an electric topic across the world—in the U.S.? in Europe? in Africa?*

A.M.: I did do a fair amount of research, but I was also nervous about doing too much. I have an interest in immigration issues, particularly those facing Western Europe. I was naïve when I arrived in France, and I learned a great deal by living there, so I think of all those years paying attention, coming out of the Métro and into groups of protesting *sans papiers*, traveling, talking to people about their lives, all of that counts as research. Still, I'm far more drawn to characters than I am to issues. Which is to say, I'm more interested in stories than policy. I feel paralyzed by too much information, by too much fact, and I think careful observation of the people around me is usually the best form of research.

O.H.: *As I imagine many who have read the book do, I would like to see myself aligned with the compassionate man on the beach who slips her a big bill. If, however, I'm being honest, I might more closely resemble a privileged vacationer who hardly notices Jacqueline at all. Did writing this novel change you in that sense?*

A.M.: I'd been living in Los Angeles, which is one of the most cosmopolitan cities in the world, but it was my native city in my native country. I was lulled by its familiarity, and I'd lost that critical eye. Moving to Paris woke me up. And then when I started work on this book, yes, I was changed further. I could no longer ignore what was convenient to ignore. Not because I was some noble crusader for good, but because it served my work. Still, I was always watching, and while it was mostly out of self-interest, it certainly provided me an empathy I wouldn't have had otherwise. That's what I like so much about writing. I think of it as a kind of war against insularity, against complacency, and against willful blindness. I've always hated writing that celebrates the closed circuit, the narrow perspective, writing that denies the existence of other people, other problems. Why write other than to know in some way the difficulties of other people's lives?

O.H.: *The principal characters in both of your books are temporary inhabitants of their environments. Did you grow up in one place? Do you travel widely now?*

A.M.: We moved from California to Idaho when I was fourteen. Hardly a peripatetic childhood, and nothing compared to many people I know, but I do think that moving at that time had some impact on the way I see the world. I've traveled a great deal since then, and have lived in many different places. I keep saying that I'd like to stop traveling so much, but I don't seem to stop. It's exhausting, but it's also a privilege to be able to live this way, and I love it. There's no question that my writing has been formed by what has increasingly come to feel like a transient life, by so consistently finding myself on the outskirts of one world or another. I do wonder which came first—being a foreigner or being a writer.

O.H.: *I see both Camus and Hume in this story.* ["*Half a man's life is spent in implying, in turning away, and in keeping silent. Here the actor is the intruder. He breaks the spell chaining that soul, and at last the passions can rush onto their stage. They speak in every gesture; they live only through shouts and cries. Thus the actor creates his characters for display. He outlines or sculptures them and slips into their imaginary form, transfusing his blood into their phantoms.*" —*Albert Camus,* The Myth of Sisyphus.] *The actor is aware that he is pretending to be what he is not. So, too, is Jacqueline's survival farce: she is completely conscious as she adopts the physical gestures of someone who is carefree and content. Her reality is the extreme opposite of that. She intuits, however, that she must play the part in order to function acceptably even on the fringe of society. Did Camus enter your mind when developing this character? The novel?*

A.M.: I did think of Jacqueline as a sort of actor. As with all stories of immigration, I knew *Marker* would be a story of reinvention and therefore a story of theater. She's a master of disassociation, but I wasn't thinking of Camus. I'd had enough of him with *You Deserve Nothing,* or so I thought. But who knows what seeps in, what lingers on? If anything, I think it was his lyrical essays about Tipasa and about the sea that influenced this novel.

OH: *More than most characters, Jacqueline is an embodiment of David Hume's suggestion that the self is solely a bundle of perceptions. In other words, Jacqueline is who she is because of who she has been. You have proven yourself an agile writer, vis-à-vis writing from different perspectives—both in this novel and in* You Deserve Nothing, *in which you created three separate narrators. Does perspective play an important role in your new novel as well?*

A.M.: It does, yes. In fact, I think perspective is its central subject. I'm wary of saying more.

O.H.: *William Trevor began his adult life as a sculptor and later described his writing as chipping away at a block of marble. Are you a chipper or a builder? In other words, do you chip away at a block of writing, or are you more methodical, building up the block brick by brick?*

A.M.: I'd like to know what Trevor means exactly. Does he have a fully formed story in mind when he begins? Does he then cut away at it? I certainly don't work that way. I barely know a thing about plot when I begin, and whatever I intend to write is never what I write. I suppose I'm more of a brick-by-brick writer, but to suggest that this is some kind of considered method would be dishonest. I really don't know what I'm doing. I go primarily by feel.

◆

O.H.: *What was your first publication?*

A.M.: The letter of the month in *Surfer* magazine.

O.H.: *Five books you are reading or thinking about now?*

A.M.: *The God of Small Things*, by Arundhati Roy
     Cover, by Peter Mendelsund
     Don Quixote, the Edith Grossman translation
     Green on Blue, by Elliott Ackerman
     Love Me Back, by Merritt Tierce

O.H.: *If you had to inhabit a fictional world, what would it be (i.e., the environment of which novel or short story)?*

A.M.: *The Folding Cliffs*, by W. S. Merwin

O.H.: *What's the most interesting day job you've had (from the perspective of a writer)?*

A.M.: Pizza delivery in Los Angeles.

O.H.: *You've written two novels. Have they taken a similar amount of time?*

A.M.: They both took a little more than three years to write.

O.H.: *Energy?*

A.M.: I think they took the same amount of energy, yes, but of different qualities.

O.H.: *Best advice regarding writing?*

A.M.: Travel alone. Do not be seduced by notions of a binary world. Remember that the only writing life is a life in which you write constantly. No city, no party, no bar, no notebook will make you a writer. Be furious. Write what terrifies you.

O.H.: *Your books have great titles. Were they your first choices?*

A.M.: Thank you. They were, yes. I had lists of other titles for each, but in both cases I returned to the first.

O.H.: *Summed up in a sentence, what are you working on now?*

A.M.: A novel set in a prison town.

O.H.: *What's an interview question you have never been asked that you wish you had been?*

A.M.: From the Proust questionnaire: What do you consider the most overrated virtue? ◆

Mu Cao

THREE PUBLIC TOILETS IN TA WAN

(translated by Scott E. Myers)

The people around Ta Wan Street are a bunch of degenerates
peddlers without work, prostitutes, homosexuals
even some Falun Gong practitioners
one old musician who's going deaf
two nameless painters with VD
three private clinics give local schoolgirls
painless abortions each day

Each day I go to the nearest public toilet
each day I have breakfast across from it
morning is when the sun rises
morning is when it's time to line up for the toilet
and when it's time to line up for food
I hate waiting in line
so I have to wait till evening to crap
in an open air public toilet
where a light bulb shared by male and female sides
lights up rows of piss buckets with broken handles

When the first public toilet is occupied
I go to the second one
when the feces in the second one begins to overflow
I go to the one that's farthest away and most hidden

When all alone shitting in public toilets, I like
to look at the graffiti and dirty limericks scrawled on the walls
these obscene poems
these big round breasts and huge cocks
call up the most primitive power from the depths of my life
——that's why I'm never constipated!

Liu Waitong

ON ANHUI NORTH LANE
I KISSED A GIRL

(translated by Audrey Heijns)

On Anhui North Lane I kissed a girl
She told me she needed ten thousand dollars
to keep alive the monster on her body
sometimes she makes love with an old man
who likes her Henan accent
She stole a piece of metal from the Bird's Nest
to buy a bottle of Robust Energy Drink
but her brother in Dengfeng
has lost the taste of youth

On Anhui North Lane I kissed a girl
Back then I was a very poor guy
She said it doesn't matter
She will never be able to earn ten thousand dollars anyway
to give to the government that cares so much about her
sometimes when she makes love with an old man
she calls on her slightly unsightly sisters
and while the lights of Anhui bridge are still dimmed
they strip off their scars and skin black

On Anhui North Lane I kissed a girl
the dust dilutes the salt of her lips
dawn distorts the shape of her breasts
newspapers leave ink stains on her fingers
the video camera consumes her
from head to toe, all that remains is ten thousand dollars
like a rumor, a testimony to the country's happiness

Mu Cao

MY TEACHER AND I

(translated by Scott E. Myers)

My teacher and I
Met and fell in love at Zijingshan Park
I appreciated the gentle temperament of a mature man
He appreciated my youthful fire and wicked desires

He says the world is very big
We should go outside and look around
That's how one wards off sadness
We should go to a gay bathhouse in Beijing
And experience group sex with a hundred people
Or go to Dongdan Park, or Sanlihe, or Madian
And know a different kind of lust
If I could visit Yellow Crane Tower
I'd have new inspiration for writing poems

He says all the great artists
Were fine comrades like us
Schopenhauer and Nietzsche were fine comrades
Shakespeare, Cao Xueqin and Qu Yuan were fine comrades
Rimbaud, Rilke, Yesenin and Whitman were fine comrades
Socrates, Plato, Alcibiades, Sappho, Wilde
Rousseau, Foucault, Dostoyevsky, Mayakovsky, Rodin...
Whoever despises homosexual love is ignorant!

Once my teacher read a newspaper with tears in his eyes
He wanted to know about Mao Ning's injury
About Leslie Cheung, who's doing just fine
And about whether my cock could get hard on a winter's night

He told me to read three novels
Jean Genet's *The Thief's Journal*
Ōe Kenzaburō's *Our Generation*
And Pai Hsien-yung's *Crystal Boys*
I read Allen Ginsberg's poems aloud for him

As the spring sun rose
My great teacher and I
Made ecstatic love
On a secluded bed of flowers
I ejaculated a winter's worth of semen
Into his burning throat
He didn't let himself swallow it all
And fed me leftovers——mouth to mouth

It was the first time I had tasted my own sperm
Neither bitter nor sweet
It was salty——like the taste of the sea

Tally Brennan

THE ORIGINAL

The Viet mom don't talk the talk.
Pull up them saggy pants. You gonna walk.
Take big bother's T-shirt off. Tie your shoes.
Us going to the high school? Crazy-ass news.
Mad worrified about First Born's fate,
Me già grabbing Second Son to translate.

Yeah. Anh Dung had his name all over the TV. Now everybody knows my brother can't cut it. Eleven kids in the hospital, all Vietnamese, but Anh Dung got it worst. Broken leg. Broken nose. Concussion. Did he even make a fist? Negatude-no-mundo. Vietnamese guys don't fight back. Why they get no respect.

Two detectives came to the house. Gang-control officers from the criminal intelligence unit. Big dudes with blinged-up badges on chains around their necks. Won't drink tea. Won't sit. Not on beds, and beds is all we've got in the room that isn't our kitchen. Two beds, the TV, the family altar. Me già's ironing board. Plus bags and bags of other people's dirty clothes. They say Anh Dung got hurt in a gang war. Lil Sundogg say no way.

Only gang First Born hangin' with be
Book monkeys at the library.

Cha slaps me for disrespect but cops don't pay no attention. Just write the address of the hospital. Leave.

Who can go? Not the parents. Cha working two jobs. Me già fighting for machines at the Laundromat. No kid allowed in without an adult. Should be the other way around, right? Fo sho. Fo sheezy.

Shit. At my school, somebody gets jumped every day. In the stairwells, the bathrooms, the lunchroom, wherever they catch some Asian kid alone. Even the girls get active. Middle-school black girls are tough. Most of them are bigger than me but I deal. Stand tall. Look in their eyes. Open my mouth and let Sundogg rhyme them dizzy.

We walk round and round the whole outside of the school, Me già searching for a door that opens, me dragging behind, wishing I could disappear when she finds it.

> *Got an appointment? asks the inspector.*
> *That's no temple gate. It's the metal detector.*
> *Thinking to bring a gun or knife?*
> *Can't have no weapon, not to save your life.*
> *No cop free to walk you down the hall.*
> *Just follow the signs for the principal.*

The high school is huge, man, big as a city. Corridors a block long and wiii-fucking-ide, with tile up the walls and dusty curls of ceiling paint hanging. Brown patches in the green floor. Busted lockers bolted over with plywood. Bars on the library door where glass used to be. Old-timey desktop computers in there. No books.

The bell goes off, exploding in the empty hallway, hammering, hammering, trying to beat our skulls in. Me già closes her eyes, covers her ears, folds over like she caught a bad bellyache. Loud noises do that to her.

I take off before the second bell rings and a thousand of them come charging out into the hall, run up behind, start that smack in the back of the head, so quick and slick no adult ever catch the trick.

Lucky Lil Sundogg can read on the run. WELCOME CENTER FOR NEW AMERICANS. PEER MEDIATION CLUB. MUSIC ROOM. ART ROOM. COLLEGE ACCESS CENTER. See the lights turned off inside. Know without trying. Those doors are locked.

Way at the end of the hall, a sticking-out sign says OFFICE. The secretary's head jerks up like her string got yanked. I'm standing there panting when Me finds me. She's so little, Me già, so old school. Coming here by herself, who thought she could do that?

Secretary makes me sign the book. Me già can't write. Not in any language. Because of the war and the camps and all that. Secretary needs me to pronounce my name: Cuong.

Like King Kong?

Like Vietcong, Lil Sundogg says. Me's head snaps around, worried I shamed her. Cha and her have this big hate on the communists. Even dead ones. Blame all the killing and torture on them.

Secretary points us to a row of plastic chairs while she whispers into her phone. We sit and look at this shrine they have. Cabinets full of basketball trophies. Ancestor portraits of important men. Judges, professors, generals graduated from here, back when they wore suits with wide lapels and neckties like bibs. Not one important guy is Asian. Or black.

Finally we go in.

Behind this big-ass wooden desk is a lady. *Nguoi da den*, Me whispers, like I can't see the principal is black. A bodacious African-American lady, sitting up on her high-backed throne like a queen, with her extra-long neck and gold hair cut close to her skin. There's a leather sofa and a banquet table with chairs, like the lady lives in her office. This time, the seats we sit in are soft.

Here we're facing the new shrine. A wall of pictures in golden frames. Lady Principal with Oprah. With Tavis Smiley. With the mayor. Her and some other people with the President of the United States. I recognize Martin Luther King, Jr., alone by himself. And Nelson Mandela before he died.

Lady Principal leans forward on her elbows to look. Maybe she's never seen anything like us before, either. What I see, down her blouse, behind a waterfall of silver chains, is a set of double-D tatas.

> *Important black lady start to frown.*
> *Me già don't know she gettin' put down.*
> *Me's plaid blouse don't match her plaid skirt.*
> *Both together make your eyes hurt.*
> *Middle of winter, wearing sandals with socks.*
> *Lady Principal's dangly earring rocks.*
> *You need to see me, Mrs. Kong?*
> *I have another meeting. I don't have long.*

Nguyen, I say. Our family name is Nguyen. Nguyen Anh Dung is my brother. The one in the hospital? I spell for her so she can find him on her computer.

Yes. I see. Lady Principal looks at us, eyebrows perked up, puzzled, like why are we here? If we're worried about Anh Dung keeping up with his assignments, we should have the hospital social worker give the secretary a call.

Say his leg is broken in two places, Me whispers. Say his head aches. He can't think.

> *Big bro can't think. Did he ever?*
> *Obedient son never learns to be clever.*
> *Cha rules the family. He wears the crown.*
> *Wife and children got to bow down.*
> *Told where to work and who to marry*
> *Part of the baggage First Born must carry.*
> *More of the message he reads on the page:*
> *Support the parents in their old age.*

Him all skinny and hairless and pale
Knows he ain't allowed to fail.
Have the right answer, say yes sir,
Be best in the class, become a doctor.
The only thing he can control?
Lil bro, like he own my soul.

First Born allowed to make Second Son do stuff for him. What's fair about that? The delivery-boy bike was too heavy. I told him. Snow in the street. Ice at the stop signs where cars were spinning their wheels. Big fucking crash in the crosswalk. Car horns blasting. Underwear spread around in the wet. Ironed shirts run over and torn.

Who got blamed? Who got slammed upside the head? Me già didn't say one thing, just stood in the corner shaking, like she's having another malaria flare-up. Anh Dung never looked up. Never said he was the one made me go. Just kept turning those pages, studying for his Spanish test, memorizing more words he can't get his mouth around.

Lil Sundoggy-dogg, he don't care.
Us gonna be a hip-hop millionaire.

The reality is, Mrs.—Lady Principal's eyes slide over to her computer screen—Mrs. Dung, this incident occurred at a public bus stop. Off school property. Outside school hours. The District does not consider it a school safety issue. Your son is not eligible for transfer. Not her problem, I tell Me già.

As I'm sure you know, this is a neighborhood school. We reflect the community we serve. Our population is over sixty-nine percent African-American, less than seven percent Vietnamese. There may be some sense of trespass, violation of territorial boundaries. Lady Principal stops, waits for me to catch up.

I know the word for land, O.K.: *dat*. But territory? Not exactly. Anh Dung is all about *ngon ngu Viet nam*. Not me. I talk American. This school belongs to *My goc Phi*, I tell Me.

It may appear—Lady strings out her words syllable by syllable, heavy with knowledge, weighing us down to where we can't argue—it may appear, to some, that immigrant students are privileged. Special classrooms. Special teachers. Special programs for English-language learners. Mandated by the state. But not funded.

Us get the best. Nothing left for the rest. Nurses, counselors, librarians gone. Art, music, sports cut to the bone. Lady Principal can't do it all. Forced to rob Peter to pay Paul.

All, Paul? No denying, important black lady can rhyme without trying.

She gives some advice from her personal life: Better not to view yourself as a victim. Run around squawking like some scaredy chicken. Not when you're considered the model minority. Check the statistics if you doubt her authority. College, job, house in the suburbs, all come to Asians in one generation. Their self-fulfilling expectation. For the native-born left behind, doing the drugs, doing the crime, one in three end up in jail, knowing from birth, they're doomed to fail.

What does she say? Me asks.

We should move to the suburbs. Suburbs is *nong thon*. Right? For a minute, I think I can ask Anh Dung but Anh Dung's not here. Just me, Cuong, the one who can't do anything right.

In the suburbs, every kid gets a computer. Every house has two cars. And a swimming pool. No more sleeping with Anh Dung. My own bed in my own room, with space for Sundogg's Akai drum machine and Bass Station II synth. Everything there growing green. Trees. Grass. You can see the sky. In the suburbs, Me già could make a garden. Grow Vietnamese mint in the ground instead of in a pot on the windowsill where it dies because there's no sun.

In the suburbs, I tell Me già, every kid goes to college. Of course she thinks that's a lie. Everything I say is lying. Like how would she know?

Cong viec. Means work, right? Is there work for us? Me isn't talking to me. She's asking the lady, her hands held out flat and empty, begging.

Lady Principal checks her watch. Me does not get the message. Lady folds her hands, thumbs twisting over and under. Me sits. Lady stares. Nobody saying nothing.

In the end, Lady Principal is the one who gives in. I can't tell you more than the police told me. A few students got involved in an ordinary street-gang dispute. No weapons were used. No arrests made. No violent incident report was filed with the state department of education. This school has been off the persistently dangerous list since I took over three years ago. A safety transfer is out of the question.

> *That story got to boomerang.*
> *Anh Dung never been involved in no gang.*

Lady Principal's head snaps up. She leans forward, staring at me. You know this how?

> *Name the gang gonna invite*
> *Some pussy rather run than fight.*

Lady Principal laughs. Gusts of laughter come rolling out. Her eyes spark. She flashes a mouthful of perfect teeth.

Freestyling ain't that easy but Lil Sundogg be feelin' breezy. And those bodacious titties jump for joy when the Lady Principal laughs.

Anh Dung got lost on the path of dharma
Spitting good deeds to plant seeds of karma.
Mellow yellow searching for enlightenment.
They breakin' on him on the cold cement.
What can the loser gain from his pain?
Never did Asians no good to complain.

The principal rises up all tall and tense and quivery, like somebody switched on her electric. Her hands slam the desk. She leans across at me. Who put you up to this?

I slide down low in my chair. My old lady, I tell her, lying on the back of my neck, looking up, all scaryfied. Me già is the only answer I have, but maybe my translation's not right.

This campaign against me has gone far enough. That cartoon in the paper this morning? That's libel. I do not barricade myself behind my office door. I'm not indifferent. Or disengaged. Anyone who imagines forcing me out will improve the racial climate here is dreaming. Or has something to gain.

I have a dream, Dogg tells her. One day this nation will rise up. An eye for an eye. Then we see who gonna cry.

Lady Principal's mouth opens but nothing comes out. The wings of her nose spread. Eyes wide-furious. Big bazongas swell and swell, sucking in air so she can yell. You do not appropriate those words! Understand? Her hands peel off the desk. Clench into fists. The lady sits, so hard the queen chair crashes the bookcase behind her. You think you've known racism? Try four hundred years. Four hundred years and counting.

Sundogg got nothing to say.

Sorry, sorry, Me già hauling on my arm, trying to drag me away. Sorry is all Me understands.

Wait, the lady say, holding her hand up to stop us before we get out the door. Your son's attendance record. Fifteen unexcused absences already this year. That's chronic truancy. As his parent, you could end up in family court.

Me già knows how many days Anh Dung stayed home to talk for Cha. But she doesn't know it's a crime. Or how many more times tough guys chased him away from school.

The district does provide alternatives for boys like your son. An alternative school gives troubled students the supervision they need. A fresh start in a work-based environment. A chance to become productive citizens. The ones who choose to cooperate.

Lady Principal flashes her perfect smile. At your request, I will support an administrative transfer. It's the best I can do.

Out on the street, Me digs steely fingers into my shoulders and shakes me, trying to rattle loose the words I'm hiding. Anh Dung will go to a new school, I say, because that's what she wants to hear.

Her skinny arms snake around me and squeeze. This doesn't happen. Not even to First Born. We're not like those TV families, all the time touching and hugging. Squashed against her bony chest, my face twisted sideways, I'm trapped. No room to move. No breath to rap. Sundogg fights free. Because Sundogg know. Alternative school's where the gangstas go.

Me grabs my chin. Her fingers hook into my cheeks. She forces my head around to make me look. Her black eyes drill down. *Bi mat*, she tells me. A secret. Cha and Anh Dung won't know we came. Not ever.

Me can have secrets? Shit. I didn't know. She can make herself separate from Cha? From Anh Dung? From me, even? I'm staring like I never saw her before, this old lady with a face fierce as a demon mask. Worry lines like a knife cut into her forehead. Another black hole where a tooth used to be. *Hu'a*. Promise. She shakes my head until the parked cars jump and I hear this weird noise in my ears.

O.K. O.K. Whatever. A promise in Vietnamese doesn't have to cross over. Me can't reach me in the American world. Dogg knows. That's the secret we have.

Me wraps her hand around the back of my neck, pushes me toward home, like she is in charge. When she has no idea. Neither does Cha. Their ignorance spreads out all around them, an ocean of helplessness with no islands, no shore. Sundogg sees hands waving above the water. Sundogg stands and watches, from someplace far off.

I'm good at secrets. I could be cool with not telling Anh Dung, because then I'd have to apologize, wouldn't I? Tet is coming, the time to pay debts, fix mistakes, start over. If I don't make it up with Anh Dung, Tet won't be the same.

We stop on the corner by Anastasi's Seafood. On the sidewalk is a basket of live crabs, their red and blue legs scrabbling, struggling to climb up and over each other, struggling to escape. Me già lets go my neck. Dogg keeps a lookout for the Cambodians who work in Anastasi's ice house. Cambodians are different. Cambodians do gangs for real. Real drugs. Real guns. Real killing.

Red light turns green. We make it to the safe side of Jackson Street, where I can think more about Tet, remember the celebrations I loved, back when I was a little kid. Then, Cha lifted me up in his arms to watch the lion dance. Drums pound pound pounding. Cymbals clash.

The lion bows. He leaps. He shakes his head. Huge lion eyes see the lettuce hanging beside people's doors. His jaws open. Red lips. Big square teeth. Green leaves scatter. Evil spirits get scared away.

Every year, Tet comes back the same. Same smells of cooking, flowers, incense. Five fruits on the altar to welcome the ancestors. Lucky money for kids, to spend however we want. All night, firecrackers pop-pop-pop. Clouds of smoke in the streetlight. Drifts of red paper along the curb in the morning. First morning of the new year. Spring begins, even if there's snow on the ground.

> *Sundogg say the whole deal is fake.*
> *No American kid likes sticky rice cake.*
> *Or praying to the ancestors for protection.*
> *Even Anh Dung got grounds for objection.*
> *Better luck to be born an orphan,*
> *Free to be your own kind of person.*

We walk past the Chinese restaurant with the gold-painted plastic columns and phony roof tiles stuck on its cinder-block walls. By myself, I would cut through their parking lot, check out the hole where the blacktop fell in. That hole so wide and deep it already swallowed the plastic barricade they stole from the water department. People have weddings here anyway. The ones who haven't moved to the suburbs.

The time we went, Me già wore *ao dai*. Long, red, with high collar and gold embroidery up the front. Even though it's so dark inside you can hardly see. They played that whiny, off-key, nose-singing music with the boring, boring beat. Me loved it. She loved the waterfall that comes down from the ceiling and splashes into a concrete pool. All behind it is painted black, so you know they're hiding something, but Me said how beautiful, with the spotlight shining through filters that turn, making the water pink and then blue and then gold. *Mot bai tho.* A poem. Me saw a beautiful poem. That's what she wanted to see.

What Me does not want to see is Lil Sundogg. Even though he's not genuine black, Dogg keeps me from being genuine yellow. Two together make an original, a two-toned, tiger-striped new breed of animal. Camouflaged for sun and shade, dancing in the space rhyming made. I see you but you don't see me. Open your eyes to reality. Let go your grip on what used to be. Learn to sail in uncharted territory.

Find Second Son got there first.

Yeah! ◆

Andrew Grace

SELF-PORTRAIT AS A NAIL IN THE BOTTOM OF A RIVER

There are moments that open
in halves like a shotgun
and some that spin like a chip of tungsten
in vinyl grooves. This one weeps
like a fuse. In it, my parents
are weaving a clot of wires.
The power is out and they are
trying to coax volts out of a tin box.

My brother and I circle the water heater
like a maypole and stomp its pellets
into grist. The power might never
come back on. We will thrash
in the basement while my parents
pass a red wire between them forever.

◆

The river is copper and buckshot
that the nightbirds swallow for ballast
as they leave to scour punk board for grubs
at the lumber yard. In the parking lot,
a truck idles, and I am inside it, waiting
for Toby to return from stealing
power tools. He is building a house
without a permit in an unzoned lot
beyond our land. He wrestles a Sawzall
and sander into the bed and we drive
past the lights of the salvage yard
to where we'll make rooms in the dark.

Toby's teeth are a mess, but there's a reed
in there somewhere that lets him
sound out "Something Sweet, Something Tender."
He wants to make a dining table
big enough to seat everyone he loves
before he builds a roof. I help him,
knowing the house will never be finished.

◆

Toby damns his right hand
for being unsteady on the table saw
he runs off of his truck's battery.
I am afraid that my hammer
will bring police, so I hit lightly.
What we build will be burned
by the housing commission,
our stolen nails falling
from black wood like sparks
from a fuse that failed to fire.

◆

Our power does not come back until March.
My parents burn all the cheap wood
including my old changing table,
its nails sifted and laid out on a sill to cool.
Later, I pocket them and sneak down
to the river to throw them like darts
at the shadows. The scent of moss
and the echo of jake brakes. The nails
gathered at the bottom of the river
like a creel of minnows. Our valley
gave up its iron a long time ago.

Jeffrey Gustavson

THE LITTLE ICEBERG

Skull and world, a gowk and a titling: after a few thousand hours of mute acquaintance, we were friends for life; but how to navigate the captious skerries, cast beyond the allure of specifics? That my father, who was born in the United States and never set foot in Sweden, was nevertheless in some crucial sense Swedish, a notion I comprehended before I could write—maybe even before I could speak—was probably the first abstraction ever to have crystallized in my understanding. Integral to the concept, no doubt, was my awareness of the proximity of numerous Swedish relatives, spanning several generations, the oldest of whom spoke to one another, and to my father and his siblings, almost exclusively in that quaint, musically vowelled language.

Farmor and Farfar, the names we called my grandparents by—Swedish diminutives for "father's mother" and "father's father"; those of our cousins whose mother was our father's sister would call them Mormor and Morfar, of course, and perhaps my grasping of this semantic subtlety was the first stage of the crystallization—lived across the street from us, on West 22nd Street, in Jamestown, New York, one of the densest American settlements of Swedes east of Minnesota. Half the city, it seemed, was Swedish.

Great Aunt Agda, my grandfather's sister, who was a widow by the time I was born, lived about twelve blocks away, in a house full of solid old furniture, with dark wallpaper in all the rooms and a heavy burgundy drape across the doorway of the staircase to the second floor and a heavy, old-fashioned, squarish Bakelite telephone on a stand in the hallway, which I'd sidle off to and pretend to talk on whenever we visited her; I must have been trying to reach someone from the Sweden of long ago which her house evoked.

My father had ten brothers and sisters, and all except the two youngest, Uncle Darwin and Aunt Alice Ann (whom we called Aunt Elsie), were already married by the latter half of the fifties, when I was small, and had begun having children of their own, so I took an extensive and ever-growing network of cousins for granted as well. My father's parents owned a three-story wooden house on a lot the size of two or three ordinary West 22nd Street lots. Their front door was almost exactly opposite ours. The dining room was at the back of the house, and its rear wall was dominated by a mullioned window bordered with white lace curtains. Another wall was filled with shelves that my grandfather had built, on which my grandmother kept her elaborate collection of bric-a-brac: colorful glass vases, ornate demitasse cups, snuff boxes made of leather and bark, Dala horses, figurines of other animals and of birds and tomtes and gnomes, glass and stone and metal paperweights, and a number of curios that my grandfather had made (including a miniature log cabin, painted dark red, constructed of wooden lollipop sticks, and equipped with a shingled roof, a chimney, windows with panes of glass in them, and a door that featured the *pièces de résistances*, two tiny hinges and a working skeleton-key lock, all made of brass; on special occasions, Farfar would take the cabin down and, using a delicate pitchfork he had fashioned out of wire, slide a burning pellet of incense onto a platform inside and close the door, and a plume of dense white smoke would curl out the chimney for twenty minutes or so).

QUARRYMAN

The land our house stood on had once been my grandfather's, and, before that, for all I know, *his* father's—at the top of our street was the house, the shop, and the storage yard of a gravestone business that had been run by my father's grandfather, August Gustavson, who was a monument maker for the Lake View Cemetery, a short way up the hill from our street, and for other graveyards within a hundred-mile radius of Jamestown. He had learned his profession in Sweden, where he was a quarryman, and immigrated to America in 1907, settling first in Quincy, Massachusetts, where he perfected his knowledge of stone-carving.

We kids spent countless hours clambering over the blocks of granite and marble that spilled down the hill beside the shop, and were as familiar with the intricacies of that boulder pile—toeholds, ledges, grottoes, tunnels—as any scholar of Mont-Saint-Michel, or any Alpine first-ascender. It was our Matterhorn, and we its mountain goats.

My father once told me that several of his grandfather's fingertips had eventually become stubs, from getting crushed between blocks of stone in the course of his work, and how strange it felt when he playfully pinched his grandchildren's ears with them. In all surviving photographs of him from middle age onward, he has his left hand tucked out of sight in his pocket or behind his back.

My Aunt Elsie recently confirmed this digital mutilation, and added, "Oh, he was strong as an ox. He liked to drink beer sometimes, you know, and one day he took the trolley to Brooklyn Square to go to a tavern, and he asked the trolleyman to wait for him while he went in for a beer. The driver said, 'I can't do that, I have a schedule to keep,' so Granddad got out and lifted the trolley car off the tracks and went in and had his beer, then came out, put the trolley back on the tracks, and rode home."

TAURINE PUFFS OF AIR

My brother Dann, our parents' firstborn, was the great experiment, the test case of their child-rearing theories, the breaker of filial trails that I then had the good fortune to walk on. Slides of him in a season that's clearly spring show him bundled up in long pants, a sweater, and a hat, while in corresponding later shots of me I'm in shorts and a T-shirt, and hatless; indeed, we both were by then. He was a very tolerant and solicitous older brother, as brothers go, during essentially every phase of our childhood and youth. In an emblematic image, the two of us are seated, entirely absorbed in the moment—a giraffe, or President Eisenhower, or a giraffe with President Eisenhower clinging to its neck, could have sauntered past and we wouldn't have noticed—on the back steps of the West 22nd Street house: in his right hand is half a blue Popsicle; in one of my hands is a Fudgesicle, and in the other, the other half of Dann's blue Popsicle.

My brother's and my room was on the downhill side of the house, with a double window looking out on the steep, tree-covered slope that separated our yard from that of our neighbor, Mrs. Harvey, a friendly old woman with a ceramic birdbath, its bowl stained dark green from generations of algae, near her side porch (which was covered with a profusion of leafy vines that clung to the house's stucco, almost completely obscuring the windows, all the way to the roof). Dann's bed was the plush settee of a faded mauve-and-moss-green davenport with stylized floral motifs shaved into its nap; my bed had a barracksy iron-post frame painted black, and in the middle of the headrail I'd placed a decal of a roaring polar bear, which my Uncle Darwin had brought back for me from a tour of duty with his Army unit in Alaska.

My bed had much the springier springs, so was the preferred one for trampolining on, whereas Dann's had the virtue of extremely slippery casters, making it ideal for giving each other short, violent rides across the room. His bed was also equipped with two long, flexible rectangular cushions, and these served admirably as jousting cudgels—we could bash each other with them as hard as we liked without causing injury. The cushions were about the same size as we were, so we'd sometimes deem them adversaries and cuff them around like cartoon bullies and wrestle them down to the floor with our legs wrapped around them and punch and choke them till they were utterly subdued. The two cushions piled one on top of the other also made a very serviceable horse, espe-cially with a jump rope or an old necktie of Pa's looped around one end of the top cushion, to act as reins.

We slept in the same room, wherever we lived, all our lives till he went off to college, and as kids travelled to school together most of the time, ate together, played together, took baths together; though there were mornings when our need for relief from forced intimacy was great enough that we'd build a wall of cereal boxes between ourselves while eating breakfast, our scraps and arguments were rare, our fights even rarer, and any that Pa caught wind of were swiftly dealt with, generally in one of two ways: either he'd give us both dingbats—a few swats on the butt with his hand or a Ping-Pong paddle (he had little patience for parsing out blame between us, or listening to accusations and counter-accusations)—or he'd set two chairs a few feet apart and facing each oth-er, and make us sit in them till we could "look at each other again." The latter was by far the more common approach, and we'd generally start out sullenly looking anywhere *but* at each other, slouching martyrishly, arms clamped across our chests, exaggerated frowns contorting our fac-es, taurine puffs of air whooshing in and out of our eloquent nostrils, till one of us would cast a furtive and challenging glance at the other, catch him doing the same, and we'd both burst out laughing at the needless-ness of our predicament.

There was no apologizing or lugubrious reconciliation or any of that, no sermon from Pa; we'd just resume being brothers. We always had ex-tensive freedom of action within the domestic sphere, and Pa would give us plenty of warning when we were overstepping one bound or another; he'd generally say "that's enough of that," when the misdemeanor was mere companionable rowdiness, or "all right, knock it off," when our bickering threatened to escalate to all-out conflict.

THE HORSEHEAD NEBULA IN ORION

My brother had learned to read by the time he was three, and con-sequently found kindergarten—at the Euclid Avenue School, a few blocks away, a couple of streets over from the entrance to the cem-etery—absurdly boring. He hated going to school, since the educational atmosphere at home was so much more congenial. He'd mope or cry or otherwise resist going nearly every morning, and was generally pretty glum when he returned. My mother later used to say she always wished she could send me in his stead, since I was so eager to go and would have thrived among all the other kids. One afternoon when Dann got home, she asked him, "What did you do in school today?" and he an-swered, listlessly, "Put pegs in a board."

Exhibiting a stoicism beyond his years, Dann found a way to tolerate the matrix of inanity that enmeshed him. One unusually warm day in the late winter, when his class was outside during a fire drill, he stood reading aloud various phrases visible on the different parts of a fire truck. His teacher noticed, and when the drill was over and the kids were all back inside, she pursued the matter, selecting a simple picture book and asking him to read it. He easily did. She thought that perhaps he had the same book at home and had merely memorized it, so she fetched other children's books, from the first-grade room, and of course he could read those, too. She ascended the scale to sixth-grade material—the zenith of what was available in the building—and he read those books as fluently as the Dick-and-Jane stuff.

One thing led to another, and eventually the principal called my parents and breathlessly announced that their son, could they imagine, knew how to read! Yes, we know, they answered. They hadn't wanted to make a fuss about his precocity, not wishing to appear boastful. It wasn't long before the teacher had Dann reading to the rest of the class during story time, and eventually he was taken downtown for a session with a school psychologist; during the Rorschach test, when asked what one particular inkblot reminded him of, he answered, "the Horsehead Nebula in Orion."

Neither his teacher nor the psychologist had ever heard of the Horsehead Nebula in Orion, and so, the story goes, they both ended up enrolling in an astronomy course at the community college, to fill in that gap in their education. As one result of this episode, Dann was promoted to first grade; as another, my parents steered clear of teaching me to read, thinking to spare me an ordeal like Dann's, so I remained illiterate till I got to first grade myself.

FLAME-THROWER EYES

Dann and I had a shaggy green rug in our room, about three feet by five feet, faded from many washings, and with a worn-out backing. On cold or rainy days, or when we were tired of playing outside, we'd sometimes put this rug in the middle of the floor, and one of us would balance on the toes of one foot in the middle of it and twirl around, twisting it into a heavily forested mountain landscape with several steep ridges radiating out from the central caldera. We had authored our impromptu orogenies often enough to have developed a virtuoso's disdain for even minor fallings short in the execution, and would not hesitate to flick the landscape flat and re-torque it with one nonchalant pirouette after another until we were entirely satisfied. We'd then get out our box of animals—exotic African species, mammals and birds of the North American woodlands, traditional farm critters, as well as a fearsome array of dinosaurs and an alphabet of dog breeds from beagle to wolfhound—and begin manufacturing elaborate adventures for them in this verdant, treacherous world.

Early on, we'd have to decide whether or not to allow the conflation of geological epochs—could the dinosaurs mix with the modern animals?—and after that the story could begin to unfold. The impulse to organize the beasts into armies of some kind was always strong, though not invariably determinative, but if that was to be our framework, solemn and painstaking efforts would be devoted to maintaining parity as the troops were mustered one by one, as in choosing up sides to play baseball. The process sometimes involved protracted negotiations worthy of a late-night coven of senators, as we debated the comparative dangerousness of a rhinoceros and a polar bear, or fleetness of a zebra and an elk, or, more hairsplittingly, aerial prowess of an eagle and a pterodactyl.

All aspects of the adventure we were preparing to enact were open to discussion, and we'd each put forth provisional rules as they occurred to us—as well as assigning to the animals any special powers, temporal or spatial limitations, supplemental capabilities and the like that we deemed necessary (as in a case, say, where Dann had a badger and I had a lamb, since they were the last two animals in the pool; I'd stipulate that my lamb could fly, or had flame-thrower eyes, or something along those lines, and Dann would either agree or make a counter-proposal, and we'd eventually settle on a rule).

The dramas we invented were heavily dependent on narrative, as we described in detail what each character was up to, and why, and could go on for hours, or even be carried over to the next day. We would ascribe thoughts and feelings to these mass-produced blobs of plastic as if they were more exalted and touchy than Achilles, and hatched battle plans of Clausewitzian ingenuity for our tyrannosaurs and penguins and goats.

Much of the time we'd be lying on our stomachs so the action would be at eye level, chattering on about the evolving skirmishes and regularly emitting all manner of outlandish vocalizations no system of notation ever devised could possibly hope to capture, but we would sometimes expand the field of action to other parts of the room—one or both beds, the window sills, the drawers of our bureau—and were perfectly prepared to leave one plot-line hanging unresolved while we shifted our focus to finish, or further, an earlier one; and once in a while a gleeful madness would overcome us, and we'd pull out soldiers and tanks and fighter planes and B-52s and unleash a time-dissolving Götterdämmerung wherein it was every link in the Great Chain of Being for itself, till nothing that ever breathed was left alive.

MASSIVE CALLIOPES

For all my life, my father was a newspaperman. He worked for the Jamestown *Post-Journal* for many years and in many capacities—photographer, reporter, city editor, state editor; before leaving he had become, in effect if not in name, the editor-in-chief. We kids used to relish visits to the *Post-Journal*. I know I never had any coherent notion in my childhood of what work was; I simply took it for granted that my father's job existed for the sake of our amusement, because whenever we visited he would take us to see some new, or some favorite, part of the building. I was most fascinated—and most frightened—by the press room, which, when it was printing time, was more thrillingly terrifying than anything else I could yet imagine.

The different parts of the room were connected by metal steps and catwalks and ladders, and I would hold my father's hand tight the whole time I was there, convinced that otherwise I would fall into the machinery and be annihilated. The paper came in rolls like rolls of paper towels as big as a house, and the presses themselves were as bigger than houses, and the paper tore through the rollers at a terrific speed, and the racket was much too great to permit speech.

The men in the pressroom were brawny and oily and friendly, and seemed as unconcerned about danger as my mother was when she ironed clothes. They always seemed glad to see my father, and treated him like a member of their guild. The printing process was automated except for the final stage, when the folded newspapers slid off the end of the press along steel rollers in rows of two like thick playing cards spurting from the hands of a giant magician, which the pressmen would scoop up in bunches and stack in the compartments of sturdy rectangular carts.

Once, in a solemn and carefully supervised lark, I was allowed to turn on the presses, by pushing a red button as big as a juice glass; I had to use the whole palm of my hand.

The darkrooms were almost equally fascinating. The men who worked there were more like dentists or jewelers, and the dim red lights and bottles of chemicals, and chemical smells, had a colder and more exotic appeal. I never got tired of watching the images appear on the paper floating in a pan of developer, or of climbing up on a stool to get a clearer view of the enlarger. My father had started out at the *Post-Journal* as a photographer; one night he was covering a boxing match in Erie, Pennsylvania, and one of the fighters got punched out of the ring into his lap, breaking an expensive camera.

The newsroom, where my father spent most of his time, was on the second floor. In an anteroom just past the entrance were six or seven squat, heavy wire-service teletype machines—A.P., U.P.I., and several others less well known—incessantly *kerchank*ing out news stories on scrolls of perforated paper. The machines would stamp an entire row of type at a time, or so it seemed, as narrow as a standard newspaper column, and sometimes my father would stand by the machines reading stories as they emerged, tearing off any that seemed likely candidates for that day's paper. Otherwise they would pile up in wire baskets, and every once in a while a copy boy would fetch an armful and dump it on an editor's desk.

There were also men, and a few women, at metal desks throughout the room, sitting before Underwood manual typewriters, some smoking, some with a telephone receiver clamped to their ear, clacking out stories on "copy paper," sheets of coarse-grained wheat-colored paper that was the universal medium of reporters—my father always carried a sheaf of it, folded in thirds or fourths, in his inside jacket pocket, along with several thick, soft-leaded pencils, some of them sharpened at both ends. There was also a series of suspended wires with clips attached every couple of feet which ran to various parts of the newsroom, for transporting marked-up copy from desk to desk. Jutting out from a pillar in the middle of the room was a pneumatic tube, like the kind found in department stores, for sending stories ready for typesetting up to the composing room.

The composing room was always redolent of hot metal, and the racket there was constant and deafening. Arrayed throughout the room, which occupied the whole floor, were eight or ten Linotype machines—naked contraptions alive with moving parts, like accordion keyboards yoked to massive calliopes—and an equal number of metal trolleys holding double-page galleys in which set type was being slotted and clamped into place. The men operating the machines weren't so much sitting at them as engulfed by them, each stroke on the keyboard in front of them magnified into a series of metallic crashes as another letter was molded and the glittering sentences accumulated. My father would frequently go up to proofread the galleys, and he was so adept at it that he didn't need to have a proof pulled but could read the type as it lay, backwards and upside-down.

VALUE FOR YOUR PENNY

In a hall off the back corner of the newsroom was a soda dispenser, whose refrigeration mechanism always gave off a deep vibrating hum, with the bottles of pop submerged most of the way up their necks in a large tray of chilled water and held in place by an elaborate grid of metal channels, through which you slid the flavor you wanted to buy to a metal collar into which only one bottle at a time would fit;

you released it by inserting a dime in a slot on the side of the machine and then pushing a nickel-plated lever, flanged like a shoehorn, which released the collar from around the bottle like setting some vitreous microcephalic Puritan free from the stocks. You then prised the cap off by gripping the bottle around the base and inserting the lower edge of the cap, which had been scalloped at the bottling plant to pinch it uniformly against the rounded lip of the bottle, against a curved jaw bolted to the side of the machine and levering the bottle steadily downward till enough of the crimps had been flattened out to loosen the cap, which then fell off with a plink into the hopper below. If you didn't wedge the cap in just right, only one little tent of metal would loosen and the cap wouldn't come off; sometimes it took two or three tries.

My preferred flavor was Orange Crush, but I would sometimes buy a Coke or a ginger ale (the only flavor that came in a dark-green bottle), and they were always delicious, especially the first long sip. Wooden crates for the empties were stacked next to the machine. Owing, probably, to the thermodynamic optimality of the combination of the thick glass bottles and the ice-cold water, the pop was always chilled with a coldness that seemed as close to perfection as any liquid could hope to achieve, and the various generations of soda machines I've encountered since have all fallen far short in that regard; dispensers like the one at the *Post-Journal* weren't very common even then, though I can remember them at the occasional rural gas station or general store for a few years after, but I've never seen one since; decades later, after I'd moved to New York, I once described this type of dispenser to Andy Logan, *The New Yorker*'s city-hall reporter, and after thinking about it for a little while, she said she could remember seeing them back in the forties and fifties.

No trip to the *Post-Journal* was complete without a stop at the gumball machine, a glass globe atop a heavy steel stanchion, full of colorful gumballs, which were dispensed individually for a penny apiece. You put your penny edgewise into a horizontal slot projecting out from the casing below the globe and slid a notched chrome slider about two inches to the right, and, with a satisfying snick from a hidden spring, a gumball rolled down a little chute into a little curved half-pipe with a sort of twin-tined bumper at the end that enabled you to pluck up the gumball without any risk of dropping it. You had no way of knowing what color you were going to get, of course, but that was an uncertainty I was never so egocentric that I couldn't grasp the reasonableness of, given that it was only, after all, a question of value for your penny. I preferred yellow ones, and did sometimes get them, and besides, my open-mindedness in this trifling regard became self-reinforcing, and primed me to take chances with my presumed preferences in myriad matters of greater consequence later in life.

We all enter the world as little philosophers, and are at every moment, whether we know it or not, enacting peripeteia in the unscripted drama of our beliefs. As with the pop machine, I was deeply, subliminally impressed with the mechanical ingenuity and exactitude of the dispensing mechanism, and the confidence I always felt that the tasty product I sought, for which I'd begin salivating before I'd even inserted my coin, would invariably be delivered seems to me now an unwitting silent paean to the last days of the purely analog era, when even the most unessential devices were engineered to *last*. And I can still recall the burst of flavor that would be released by the initial crunch, and the weird mixture of properties—dry and moist, spheroid and planar, piquant and bland, granular and homogeneous—that registered in my consciousness when I renewed the gummy mass, as I sometimes did, with a second gumball.

I was always torn between the alternatives of (a.) spitting out the comparatively insipid gum in my mouth and starting out with a fresh gumball and (b.) adopting the additive, more-is-more approach; both had so much to recommend them that it was impossible, for me, to rule out either as clearly inferior. In one story that became part of my family's lore (and enjoyed a short period of wider publicity, since my father had written it up for a column in the *Post-Journal* called 'Round About Town), I was at the paper with my father not long after my little sister Nancy was born, and a colleague of his came up and asked me, "What do you have that's new and sweet?" Smiling up at him, delighted that a man I didn't even know should take such an interest in me, I answered, in all sincerity, "A pink gumball!," holding it out on my palm. ◆

Lucy Biederman

MY DESTRUCTIVE IMPULSES

The football team practices in the middle of the night
with the stadium lights on so hard you could gag. The air
just sits there like a big fat jerk. Open the windows within
the windows, roll the cool moon through the street. Mold-
flecked oilcloths hang from soft wood tables, ceiling fans
barely turn. It's useless to fall in love here, where no one
thinks of the future. I don't believe in parties but if I did I
would pray for a huge one tomorrow, open to all comers,
wobbly bike riders to '70s homesteaders. I would tell God
to tell everyone there to try a little harder from now on.

Earle Sebastian

SWANKERS

A Portfolio of Photographs

Asked to define the word "swank," Earle Sebastian said, "It's a term that would apply to someone like Miles Davis: a working-class hero who found his own way. I have an image of Miles as a young man looking at another jazz great— white individual, can't remember what his name was. Miles is in conversation with him, and Miles is looking at his jacket. I think that is really interesting, because Miles was a Swanker. He was a cat like Marlon Brando or Frank Sinatra. There are those that begin something, and there are those that follow. If your eye is on it, you can always work out who the main cats are and who the followers are. A Swanker is somebody that understands taste, somebody that understands etiquette. Somebody who is an absolute gentleman is a Swanker."

An Interview with Earle Sebastian

ADRIENNE BROCK: *Can you tell me a little bit about your history as a film-maker, photographer, and activist?*

EARLE SEBASTIAN: I was born in South Africa. I'm classified "coloured." My parents are mixed race: my father was Indian; my mother was African. My parents were forced to leave South Africa because of the Apartheid regime. There were no mixed-race marriages allowed what-soever, so my parents left for England. I grew up in East London—a very blue-collar, working-class environment. I didn't quite fit in, which was somewhat awkward as I was growing up. I think from a very, very early age, it was the arts that attracted me, but there was nothing being offered to point me in that direction.

South Africans are very, very proud people, and that's something that I kind of learned along the way as well. My mother's father, Fred, was a sailor—a Zulu man—and he used to travel all over the world. Whenever he would go back to South Africa, he would come back with hats in hatboxes from England and shoes from Europe. Fred was a very working-class African man, but he was still very dapper and well done. Apparently, according to my mother, he used to clean his shoes with a toothbrush and was very meticulous as to the length of a cuff of a shirt underneath a jacket or the way in which you wore your hat. Some of the things that got passed down to me through stories of him along the way were: Never be first at the dance. Always make sure you've got a clean white handkerchief in your back pocket, and always make sure you've got the best shoes on, and you'll be fine.

As I grew up, I took a keen interest in fashion—very much so. It was something that always interested me beyond stories of Fred, though I think, you know, genealogically, it had something to do with pride. I think that that happens a lot within the working class. So there was always a fascination with style and etiquette and elegance and grace. I spent some time in the fashion industry at a bespoke tailor's, learning the ins-and-outs of cutting shoes and ties and shirts.

Then, I started to travel around Europe. I went on a vacation to the South of France. It was supposed to be a ten-day vacation, but I ended up staying in Europe for a number of years. While I was traveling, I came across a film crew in Madrid. They were doing a series of commercials that I managed to get in on—just as a production assistant—and I man-aged to form a relationship with the cinematographer. He watched what I was doing, what I was up to, and one day he said to me, "Do you have an interest in film?" And I said, "Absolutely." We got more and more familiar with each other, and before long, I had more responsibilities.

I came up through the camera department—second assisting, first assisting—and I started operating. I started successfully directing music videos out of England. I came to N.Y.U. to study a course in light, and when I finished that course, I was offered a project here by the Red Hot Organization: a documentary on the issue of H.I.V. and AIDS called "Stolen Moments." It was there that I...found out all about H.I.V. and AIDS and how it affected my people in South Africa, not just America, but my people in South Africa and India—and of course both of those places are important to me. That documentary became very, very successful, particularly on the underground circuit, and after that, I went on to continue working here in New York, directing music videos for Mary J. Blige, Madonna, Missy Elliot, Beyoncé—a host of female artists—and I'm still here.

A.B.: *And how did you first come across the Swankers of South Africa?*

E.S.: A very good producer friend of mine, Joel Hinman, called me up one morning and said, "Have you seen today's New York *Times*?" And it was early. I said, "I haven't." He said, "Get yourself a copy and then give me a call back." Half an hour later, he called me back to ask if I'd picked up the New York *Times*, and I hadn't. He said, "Go out, get today's New York *Times*, turn to page four, column B." It was obviously important to him, so I went out and got it, turned to the page and there was the story of my grandfather—meaning, the story was based on a group of migrant workers that live in hostels on the borders of major cities—like Johannesburg, for instance—construction workers, forklift truck drivers, manual laborers, factory workers, who, as a hobby in one of these particular locations in one of these hostels housing workers outside the city, had started these very basic, competitive fashion shows where these men would collect their own wardrobe—predominantly from tailors in Europe.

I became absolutely obsessed with this story. In the article at the time, the prize for winning one of these fashion shows would be the equivalent of a ballpoint pen. If it was a larger show, the prize could be a chicken, or a goat, even—if it was Christmas—or a blanket. I was just intrigued, so I got on a plane and headed to Johannesburg, and found my way into one of these hostels and began the process of documenting this story and researching for a potential documentary. I shot moments of it as I was getting to know them. I shot stills of one particular show. I was only there for a short period of time. After I shot a group of photographs, I came back to the States with the aim of going back to do more.

But life takes over. I never managed to get back but always was in love with these photos. Then, as time went on, I started to see other stories based around various groups of men doing this stuff. I had followed my project through. I'd brought in another producer to help me craft the documentary on the Swankers. That relationship with her became a political battle over ownership of the rights for the documentary. I'd had a second team of producers come in that had funding, but the existing producer didn't want it done without her involvement, so it never happened, but these images still exist.

A.B.: *The pixel ratio seems to give the photos a grainy quality, which adds something to each piece—and just the fact that they're all in black-and-white. It kind of feels like you're transported back in time. That this might not be a recent story; it might be in this time that's separate from everything else.*

E.S.: As far as the pixel ratio is concerned, I was going for the look that you see now, but as you try to blow the image up, it distorts the quality, so you can only really get to a ten by eight without disrupting the image. Back then, I shot it digitally, and the pixel ratio wasn't what it is now. It isn't as good as it could have been. But these images still draw attention. I did want to shoot something that felt natural to the environment, so there was always that earthy quality that for me relates to Africa. It just felt natural to be shooting it dirty, for want of a better term. They're impoverished individuals. They come from this very working class environment, but the juxtaposition is the wardrobe.

A.B.: *There's a real awareness of how one holds oneself and the profiles and the angles of the body. Is that something that's part of the demonstration of the fashion pieces, and how does that awareness of the body come into play with demonstrating these articles of clothing?*

E.S.: I was absolutely blown away when I saw this. As I mentioned before, these environments were very raw. They were either basements or in and around downtown factory-type settings but in these hostels, which were old rentals that had been left abandoned for a number of years once Mandela had been released and the Apartheid regime collapsed.

These men would come out to no music on these concrete floors. The audience was completely silent. There was no music, and they would do this very elegant kind of dance, if you will, whereby they would lift a pant leg to show you a sock or to show you a shoe and the fact that the shoe had been polished. They would take off their hat and they'd spin it to show that the hat was actually from a British hatmaker somewhere in London, which gave them—

A.B.: —*authenticity.*

E.S.: Yeah. They would open their blazers to show you the lining. They would remove the blazer and hold it over their arm—like an English gentleman would—to show you their shirt, then lean in to show you their cufflinks and so they were judged not only on their appearance but how they performed.

A.B.: *So they're constructing a narrative of how they received the articles of clothing, or at least where the articles of clothing are coming from, as well as their knowledge of propriety when it comes to how this item should be worn and the respect that this item should be given—if it's a bespoke item, hand-crafted by a particular tailor.*

E.S.: Yes, but they would also show you who they were as far as etiquette was concerned. You know, they're proving that they have a white hand-kerchief in their back pocket, proving that the sleeve length is at the right measurement. Or a tie knot. They would point to a tie knot and they'd either be pointing to a full Windsor or a half-Windsor, depending on the shape of the collar of the shirt. See, that's very important. The shape of the collar of a shirt and a suit would determine whether you would wear a full Windsor knot or a half-Windsor knot, so it's showing that they fully understand the clothing they're wearing and who they are as it relates to the understanding of the etiquette that's needed to be able to wear this type of clothing.

A.B.: *And how do they acquire the items? If someone they know is headed to London, do they say, "Look up this tailor for me and see if he's got anything new," or are more of these items available locally today than in the days of your grandfather?*

E.S.: There is more availability, but that said, the clothes that they wear are not inexpensive. These guys are construction workers or very blue collar, but they save up to purchase a suit that is expensive to most any-one. That is also very much a part of working-class values: how you show yourself to the outside world. It has a lot to do with pride. I would be in their rooms with them going through their wardrobe, and I'd watch them do things like hang pieces of cardboard on the wall, and when they changed, they would take the cardboard off the wall and place it on the floor so that they would stand on the cardboard. They'd place their shoes on the cardboard. They wouldn't walk on the dirty floor in their socks. They'd have ironing boards and irons in these small quarters. So there was a whole regimen to do with looking after these clothes.

A.B.: *So, it's about accomplishment. Not only have they saved in order to be able to purchase these items, but they're showing their responsibility and knowledge of proper care. There's this whole behind-the-scenes element to it.*

E.S.: Yeah, exactly.

A.B.: *The men that are living in the hostels, are they primarily single men, or are they living away from their families in order to work at a particular job?*

E.S.: They're both. There are a lot of men there who have families that live outside the cities. They'll travel into the cities and they'll stay there for a period of a month, for instance, and you know, earn their living and go home for a long weekend. They're migrant workers, and they spend a lot of time together in the hostels.

A.B.: *What is the opinion of the surrounding community regarding these fashion shows? Are others invited in? Do they have more mixed feelings concerning what's going on, or do they embrace it?*

E.S.: During a holiday event or something like that in town, one of the acts might be the Swankers. The shows are staged mainly for the men that live in the hostels. I saw some women come in at certain points. It was interesting watching the audience and their attraction to the men who would come out and perform. Everyone would be in complete silence throughout. It wasn't necessarily a large group of people that would come from the outside environment. There might be one or two friends that would come, but there was no interference from the outside. It's something that's understood between other Africans. It's something that's understood between other blue-collar people, so it wasn't something that needed to go any wider that that.

A.B.: *You talked a little bit about the sense of pride that the men get from the performance and from sharing that with each other, and I can't help but think of voguing and the sense of community that exists among individuals featured in the documentary "Paris Is Burning," for example, and how that kind of reflects another group coming together and building a sense of self from performance. Do you see parallels between the two?*

E.S.: There is an absolute parallel between voguing and Swankers, and in fact, over the years, within the working class, these are small community things. No one ever thought that voguing was going to get any bigger until Madonna came along and put it on the map.

I've come to realize that this doesn't only exist in South Africa, but it exists across Africa. In Nigeria, it's a very, very different look, a very, very different approach. The Nigerian thing is way more colorful, but you're talking about a different group of people—a different country. The Swankers have now become, in certain circles, as established as voguing. In South Africa, there was a huge fashion community—designers and the whole thing. Swankers are now on the map for what it is that they do.

A.B.: *Do you still feel, when you go back to South Africa—physically, or through your work—that it's part of a process of personal discovery for you?*

E.S.: The very first time I went back to South Africa, which was in 1994, the year Mandela was released—it was almost like my gene memory kicked in. The sense of swank, the sense of etiquette, the sense of style, the attention to cleanliness—all those things that I learned growing up from my own family, I saw widely across South Africa. South Africans have a word for someone whom they may see and that they think is doing their thing right. In South Africa, someone will say to you—if they think you're dressed appropriately, they think that you're wearing your hat at the right tip, or you're wearing the right shoe—they'll say, "Sharp!" Or they'll say, "Sharp, sharp!" This means that you're on point. So, it's just a working-class pride thing, but I think there's something really interesting in that.

A.B.: *Why do you think that working-class pride is at the base of this appreciation for fashion?*

ES: I think attention to fashion gives a sense of identity. There's a sense of wanting to belong to a group of people. When you look at fashion over the years in England, you have punk, you have mods, you have rockers. If you go back and look at any movies from in and about the sixties, or seventies, there's a huge sense of style that relates to the working classes. It's a way of communicating.

A.B.: *So, the fashion creates the narrative for the community around them.*

E.S.: Absolutely.

A.B.: *Did anyone call you "sharp" when you were in South Africa?*

E.S.: Yeah, I have been called "sharp, sharp."

A.B.: *What were you wearing?*

E.S.: You know, it may have been something as simple as a pair of Converse, but it may have been the way I had the sneakers laced.

A.B.: *You mentioned earlier your work with AIDS activism here and in Africa. Does the AIDS issue in Africa have any relationship to your interest in fashion? Or are those interests completely separate?*

E.S.: They're separate.

A.B.: *Which takes precedence?*

ES: There are two sides to who it is that I am: there's the artist, and there's the humanitarian. I feel a strong sense of wanting to be able to help with the AIDS issue. Until there is a cure, it's hard for me to step away, but at the same time, there are other things I want to do. I want to continue my work as an artist. I'm a filmmaker first and foremost. I'm going to make movies. You get caught up with not having enough time for everything. This issue of AIDS—it's mind-blowing, the extent of it throughout Africa. I feel it's important I do something and raising awareness of the disease is what I've been doing for the longest time. It drives me mad that it takes up so much of my time, but the issue needs that much attention. So, it's a balance of trying to do both, and I'll get it done. I'll get it done.

PERSEIDS

WRITTEN AND ILLUSTRATED
BY FAYE MOORHOUSE.

SHE LAY THERE ON THE TILES
WHILST HE LOOKED ON. LEGS AKIMBO.

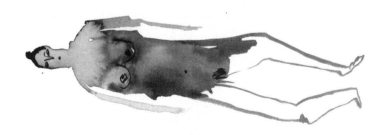

THEY WERE ONCE IN LOVE BUT
SHE JUST WASN'T SURE IF IT
HAD ALL WASHED AWAY.

THEY WALKED AND WALKED AND WALKED. TOGETHER AND ALONE.

THE DAY THE METEOR SHOWER
CAME WAS THE DAY THEY REALISED.

JUST HOW MUCH THEY WERE IN
LOVE.

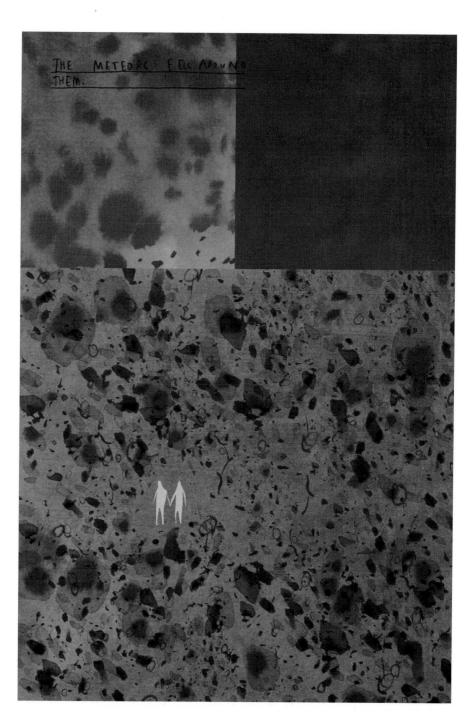

THE METEORS FELL AROUND THEM.

ARTIST'S PROCESS

I watch a lot of harrowing documentaries and films, I don't know why I like watching them but they seem to be the main inspiration for my work. I watched the film "Deep Impact" years and years ago but the feeling of it always lingers in the back of my mind; that idea of the end of the world coming, caused by a natural disaster and you have to eventually just accept your fate and die. It's sad but kind of beautiful and romantic all at the same time; this is how I wanted "Perseids" to feel.

Once I have an idea for a story in my head, I start by doing a very rough storyboard, just in pencil, so I can get an idea of how it reads as a story. I don't plan out the way the art is going to look, because it just doesn't work for me; my images come to me only when I start making them. I tend to make each piece of work in a slightly different way, using different media, but for "Perseids" I used ink. I painted each element of the image and also some background textures and then put it all together in Photoshop. I also hand drew all the text and overlaid this on the images. I spend a bit of time at this point playing around with the layout of the elements, etc. My aim is always to get a good pace going in the story: you want areas of light and dark, close up and far away— this makes it more interesting to read.

I read through it a couple of times, sit with it for a few days, re-jig some bits again, and then it's done. I've tried working in a more controlled, planned-out way in the past, where you work out how each image is going to look before you make the final artwork, but it just makes my work feel tight and horrible.

"Perseids" is about tragedy but also about love; it's often only when something truly terrible happens (in this case the end of the world) that we realize just how much we love one another.

—FAYE MOORHOUSE

THEY WERE ONCE IN LOVE BUT
SHE JUST WASN'T SURE IF IT
HAD ALL WASHED AWAY.

Epiphany
Chapbook Contest

GENRES

Fiction
nonfiction
poetry
graphic fiction

March 15th 2015
closing date
entry fee $6

Judges to be announced
Details at epiphanyzine.com

Mame Ekblom Cudd

CLEAR SPEECH

It's a bit of a wonder, the device I mean. Have you slipped it in?" Ardan whispers. He leans over the foot my bed, straightening the sheets. "You need to sit up." He's chipper. "I'll get another pillow."

I love him for whispering. Mum's at the end of the ward, staring out a window. Still, I don't want her to hear. Bored she is, I think, misses the bustle of the farm.

"Oh," I finally answer him. I want to say no, but I can't. I'm surprised I spoke at all. The stitches in the roof of my mouth feel ungodly tight and off center. The medicine doesn't touch the lingering pain. I've told the nuns. They smile, admiring the stoic.

Mum rolls open a casement with such force that it shudders. Anna, a round, pretty girl in the bed closest, jumps. Maybe Mum's apologizing now, can't tell. They're chatting away, as a warm breeze rushes in.

"Have you at least looked at the device, Fiona?" Ardan asks. "The doctor's amazing, don't you think?"

He lifts the device out of a white teacup. It's a bit of a thing, glinting, all silver and flesh-colored plastic. Yesterday, Dr. Simmons had marched in and apologized for it not having a proper case. Tall and ruddy, finally the back of his knuckles stroking my cheek, saying loudly, "I've got the right measurements, you'll speak, like a champ you will. You should."

Will it happen? I can't imagine, and what if it doesn't? Mum holding onto the side of the doctor's white coat as she lowered herself into a chair. She kept shaking.

"Aye," was all I could say then, all I ever say—really.

"Aye," I say to Ardan now, although I haven't even touched the thing. Saying it sounds normal, and reaching for normal is an obsession. Vowels are easy. It's the consonants that elude me. The lot of us, my parents, my twin brothers, Connie and Michael and Lizzie, just nine, aren't we all struggling for me to be normal? Consuming, I feel the guilt of it, notice it in bits and pieces. Everybody protecting, coaxing—expecting payback, too, you know. I should rise above it, have so many skills no one would notice my mouth and useless tongue. A mood has taken me. One more year at St. Ann's and then what, a stewardess for Pan Am, like my best friend Mary and I find in the glossy magazines, or a nurse or a teacher—none of it with my wreck of a mouth.

Ardan whispers again, "Hold out your hand." We both steal a glance at Mum. Does he notice that I might disappoint?

Sitting up, my legs dangle. I'm pasty white and thin from sipping broth for two days. I pull the blanket over.

"I'll get you tea later, soft bread and butter," he says, and smiles.

One of the first male nurses at Limerick Hospital—and I'll love him forever. Connie's right, 1967 is the most modern of times. Just five of us on the children's ward, and we all stare at him like he's a fairy blown in from the garden. Peter, in the next bed, keeps calling him "doctor."

He's not tall, but muscular and square jawed. I love a good jawline on a man—or woman. He's gruff, too, and scarred, a little one cuts through his eyebrow, and there's a large one under his chin. I imagine his life. Maybe he's from the tough part of Limerick, turned himself around—his parents still not over the shock.

Ardan suddenly stands up quite straight, sets his feet wide apart, and holds out the device. Maybe he was in some army? "Your nose is just the right thing, too, isn't it?" he says. "Sister Loretta told me you got it last summer."

I'm proud. It used to be flat and not a bit of cartilage. The doctors saying I had to be fully grown, I'm almost seventeen. Mum and Da, liking what the doctor could offer my defects. He used the word "create," fixing the botched work done when I was little, this time scraping away the scar tissue in my palate, scraping me into something else.

"Here, take it," Ardan says.

It weighs but a feather. I can't speak.

"Let me look at the stitches. The device won't hit the roof. No worries," he says.

Tilting back, I manage a small circle, nothing more. My jaw won't open or shut, like it's on some horribly stiff spring. As he looks, I slip the device back in the cup. Ardan's aftershave, all cinnamonlike, gives me goosebumps. I think of the boy I like from home, Thomas.

"I'll message your jaw a bit," he says, placing his hands on either side of my head.

I can't breathe, just little gulps of air. Thank God for my new nose.

Christ, it's painful—and wonderful. Touch is a fabulous thing. He looks at Mum down the way, chatting with Anna.

"It would give your Mum a thrill to see the device in and you talking properly. She's pretty, your mum, a bit posh. But, you're all from up north then, huh, farmers, cows and the like?"

He picks up the device—again. He's relentless, a pleading look on his face, holding it to my mouth. I lean back, wiping drool, feeling like a goddam horse, grunting and shaking my head. He doesn't know me. Because my speech is unclear, people think I'm not bright. I sound deaf; Mum's been interpreting, talking and chatting. Today, her blue dress hugs her waist, the fabric so delicate and light it swishes. I don't want to like it. My head throbs, the blood rushes through my ears. And what's talking, properly? My family and friends understand me mostly. Isn't that enough?

"All right, later maybe?" He returns the stupid thing, a bit of silver peeks out of the cup, taunting. Nearby there's a tablet and pencil, I could write, and a good composer I am. I could tell them off, Mum— and Ardan. But I can't write either, if anyone watches and I sense their impatience, my letters become small, my hand freezes, and it's over. I've had this problem forever. I'll just sit. I won't move or do a blessed thing.

But not a moment later, after fussing with a little boy with bruised spleen, Ardan says, "Let's have you get in an American shower, Fiona."

What's an American shower? I look at his handsome face, knowing he's thinking of Mum and every other pretty woman. And then, as if reading my mind, he says, "You know, standing up in a cubicle, the water rushing over, warm and fabulous. Just installed, they were."

Mum walks over. She laughs; they both do, like life is sweet and funny. Says she can give me a sponge bath, no need to fuss. He insists. Am I not in the room? They keep chuckling, opening their beautiful mouths. I used to cover my nose and mouth when I laughed, needing both hands. Now just one will do, because my nose is beautiful—and I'm able to touch Thomas at home at the same time, laughing at his jokes, my hand on his arm, flirting a bit, Mary and I with the boys, Thomas and Robbie walking over from Glintes a few days before the surgery, Mary's idea of a sweet distraction.

Feels good to walk, I ignore Mum and follow Ardan. He points to the shower head, then the lever. We're the same height. I want him to understand how hard I've worked to be normal, how I'm listening to his instructions. He won't have to tell me twice. No one tells me twice.

It's glorious. My arms are free and the water, fast and warm, soaks my hair, floats down and around my jaw, falls over my breasts, down to my stomach flat from so much running, running to show what I can do. The soap, everything smells like bleach. I'll be clean and disinfected. But the warmth helps. It's heavenly. My jaw moves, it opens and closes, loosens, sideways even.

My clothes I love. Tight, calf-high dungarees, Connie's white T-shirt—which I stole—and the little blue cardigan I knitted. Mum, Lizzie, and I we're mad for clothes and shoes. Lizzie can work the machine now, made herself little Bermuda shorts. We bought her new white Keds for her birthday, used them like hand puppets, she did, and danced around the kitchen, did a cartwheel, stroked her cheeks, picked up a hairbrush handle between the soles and tried to comb my hair, all the while praising their usefulness for things other than walking, making us all laugh. I want her now—and a good hairbrush. The hospital comb breaks and pulls so, and I won't look in the mirror; I never look. That night she placed the shoes under her pillow, and we both fell asleep to the scent of rubber.

Sister Loretta changed the sheets. I won't take off my shoes. I hop on the bed, feet dangling again. Mum's holding the teacup and staring into it. Softly, I call her. She looks as I point to my new penny loafers. She'd found American pennies and slipped them in. She knows I'm thanking her. A weak smile back.

"Dr. Simmons will be here in a bit," she says. "He'll want to hear you speak. On pins and needles we are. You could put it in now...have a go."

Doesn't Ardan march over from God knows where. The two of them looking at me, Mum holds out the cup, dropping the device into her palm. I pick it up and absolutely without thinking—I'm off, pushing them right out of my way. Mum shouts my full name, it echoes, "Fiona Elizabeth Connelly, come back immediately." I'm fast, a few long steps and I'm in the private toilet. I lock the door. Alone now with my stupid face and a giant mirror and the panic of what I've done, a horror, I've never defied my parents, never in such a manner. Have I clenched the device too hard, misshapen it? I gently place it next to the sink. The obvious marks on my palm are red and frightening.

Outside the door, Mum says, "Listen Fiona, come out right now. You don't have to put it in. Just don't flush it, please."

For God's sakes, why would I flush it? I'll have to set her straight. She thinks me too much of a child, wants me to stay one.

Then Ardan: "Yes, please don't flush. It's terribly expensive."

He's beautiful, but his bedside manner is awful. I flush anyway, just to annoy. They yell my name.

I look back at the stupid thing. It's not crushed, I don't think, all shiny, too, from the overhead light. I'll have to look in a mirror to slip it in. Mary's voice I conjure now, ordering me to list the things I like before I find fault with my horrid face. Two hands on the sink, I feel weak in the knees. I can't cry. I'll be a holy mess if I cry. And there I am: long strawberry-blond hair, peaked eyebrows over round, hazel eyes, and a fine shape to my breasts. Oh, but my lips are swollen and more misshapen than I recall, opening wider, my jumbled white teeth against reddish gums look awful. Still stiff, my jaw feels like it'll shatter if I go too far, the stitches are rough. My hand shakes so.

Mum rattles the door again, pleading. The device is to fit up high; four molars to hold the thing in place. Forcing it—and it's done, feels odd, but there it is, a click, like Sister Agnes when she's annoyed, my tongue touching the plastic piece, snapping, over and over, making a little suction at the top. What a funny thing? I'll have to say a word. "Tea," I whisper. There it is, the sound of it, clear. Not "ee," but "tea, I will have tea." The "l"s a bit garbled, maybe that will come later. The device doesn't really stay put. It does until I speak. Maybe Dr. Simmons can make adjustments. The air goes out of me. What do I want then? I don't know. But calm I feel, finally, the little things not perfect and neither am I, a work in progress we are. And isn't that just fine.

"Come out now, Fiona, a sister's gone for the key...please." Mum sounds small.

I find my little pad and pencil. Maybe I can write now. I need to. Mary says if you're not bold, you can act like it anyway. Leaning on the counter, I wipe the drool from my chin, and in big, loopy letters I write: *I'll speak when I'm good and ready.* No hesitation, I pull the door open. Mum grabs my arm; I wrench it back. I tear off the paper and she reads. She looks up. I write again: and not a moment too soon. She reads with Ardan looking over her shoulder; he laughs and places his hands on his hips. Mum looks forlorn. I write again: *We need to talk.* She looks, hands the paper back, then covers her nose and mouth with her hands, stifling a cry. The emotion of it, she tries so hard. I try so hard. I snap both hands over my nose and mouth, dropping the pencil and the pad, funny how that is. ◆

Xiao Kaiyu

PAGODA

A minute of wind ushers in three of rain,
then in four minutes the sky cleared. He and she
raced through the shaded, willow-cloaked boulevard,
suddenly stopping, and in a moment, sauntering forward.

They were digging into the lowlands nearby,
using a new style drill, into the dark depths, but maybe
being forced to go deeper into the darkness.
                                        The drill penetrated
the wriggling rock formation with a whir; and then
                                        maybe a womb.

They had already reached the end of the embankment.
A syringe towered before the mountain peak.
"Pagoda is a tactful name," he observed,
"for breeding a nest of children into the sky."

"My violence is a deep,
a deep penetration, raising the height of the crest,
like women putting a hat on a man."
She was starting to think he was a sleepwalker.

The wind blew for a long time, and the more the rain
                                        poured, the heavier it got.
He with his dreams, she with her doubts, they walked away.
The crew of well diggers were sticking to the walls like bats,
And the pagoda persisted in its haughty, solitary way.

MORNING

The candlewax morning
The snowball morning
Rolling, exploding, the conspirator and his mother-in-law
The vanquished morning

The spoken morning
The importunate sentence, the imperative sentence
and the morning that starts the language.
The morning of loudspeakers

The milk, eggs and pensive morning
The morning of class conflict

The morning moving all four limbs
The morning of sunlight and air, the lungs and
surface morning
The car takes off
the morning that hauls the husband away.

(translated by Christopher Lupke)

Christina Cooke

DOWN, DOWN

The water lapped up, licked my toes. I lifted my feet higher, higher. Somewhere overhead, the dull whir of an airplane engine drowned out the piercing squawk of swooping birds. He sneezed, hugged me closer. Curled up in my father's arms, I was carried out to sea. His palm felt large, abrasive against my skin as he scooped up handfuls of salty water to cool my scorching back. Shutting my eyes tighter, I wouldn't let go. I was a bad swimmer, such a bad swimmer, so I pressed my face against his neck and sucked the salt from his skin; that's as close to the sea as I'd get. My father carried me around, wading through the water as I clung to him, face in his neck, sucking the sea in.

◆

"Get up," my best friend Amy hisses in my ear.

Blinking, blinking, look around—rows of dark wooden pews crammed full of bodies squirming in matching blue. Head forward, inhale—incense, and mown grass. From my knees, stand up—feel the starched blue fabric scratching against skin. In the pulpit, the priest holds the chalice above his head, shutting his eyes as he moves his lips. A phone beeps; someone laughs; clack-clack of black shoes against tile as a nun advances to the beeping phone. Join hands, say the Lord's Prayer, sweat collecting behind knees in the muggy Texas heat.

"You shouldn't have done that," Amy says, trailing behind me.

Her voice sounds muffled, distant between people coming up behind me to surround the plastic table in the corner. Hands darting around shoulders and sneaking between backpacks, everyone reaches for the breakfast taquitos and sausage biscuits and boxes of lukewarm juice. Break time.

"Done what?" Dig through my pockets, fingers rubbing against uncapped pens and bits of lint. "You got a five?"

"You shouldn't have taken communion," Amy says.

"Make it a ten. You got a ten? I'm starving."

Amy crosses her arms. "Did you hear me?"

A boy laughs—loud, nasal, voice crackling as though unsure what register it should be in. On the other side of the courtyard, a bunch of guys peer at some magazine, the tallest leaning against the wooden cross by the wall. He looks up, waves. It's Barrett; that bastard still owes me five dollars.

Amy grabs my arm.

"Hmm?"

Amy keeps staring, unflinching.

"Yeah yeah, shouldn't have taken communion." Turn around. "Why not?"

"Because you're not Catholic."

Arms out, start shoving—find a place in the throng. "Well, you shouldn't listen to rap music."

"What?"

"Because you're not black."

"That's not the same thing."

Pushing forward, smell the bacon and melted cheese wafting from the taquitos; so close.

"Seriously," Amy says.

"Shut up."

She grabs my collar. "You could go to hell for that."

Groaning, face her. She's biting her lower lip, her cheeks surged up in a smile.

Sigh. "Whatever."

She bursts out laughing.

Smirking, wrap my arm round her neck in one big show. "Now gimme all your lunch money!"

She giggles, pulls out a five. "Wait, doesn't Lindsey or Barrett or someone owe you money?"

Grab it—smiling, smiling.

◆

The airport was on the right. From behind the tall brush the planes appeared, their engines muffling the thumping bass and waves hitting shore as they glided up, up. Sometimes people turned and watched, trying to guess what name was painted across each plane's side. *"Air Jamaica?" "No, the colors are all wrong." "How would you know?" "Air Jamaica left twenty minutes ago."* After the engines faded, long after, I'd still hear the palm leaves fluttering, admitting surrender.

Every time a plane left, my father crouched down, sinking us until the water came up to my knees. And I'd scream, but he could barely hear me over the plane, so I'd sink my teeth into the crook of his neck until he stood up. Clinging tighter, tighter, I was such a bad swimmer.

◆

Courtyard, fourth period. The nearby doors swing open, click shut. Someone kicks me in the shin. "Jesus!" Smack him, hard.

"Watch your mouth!" the nun yells.

"Easy," says Barrett as he rubs his arm. "Just tryin' to wake you up."

"Both of you, stop!" the nun yells.

Gaze flits to the ground, to Barrett. He winces, keeps rubbing his arm. Lean over, shoulder brushing against his. "Sorry."

Sitting in rows on the cobblestone ground, we gaze up at the nun as she paces by the cross.

"He died for all our sins," she says. "Let Himself be nailed to that cross to save us all." Behind her, the wooden cross creaks in the breeze, the timber black and rotting. "He died because He loved us," she says, "so much so that He made the ultimate sacrifice." Punched into the wood are hundreds of tiny holes, pockmarks marring the grain. "Each one of these holes," she says, "is a mark of our sin and a sign of His love." She swivels her gaze left, right; someone yawns. "Can you imagine feeling a love that great?"

Smirking, whisper to Amy, "So why couldn't I take communion?"

"Shut up," Amy whispers.

"If I helped nail Him to the cross, and He died for me, then why can't I—"

"Shut up!" she hisses as she leans forward. "Think this is gonna be on the test?"

Strands of her hair fall free from her ponytail, curl against her collar in ringlets of brown. She tucks her hair behind her ear then squints.

"Why're you staring at me?" she says.

"You have moles."

"What?"

"Right here." Reach out, finger to her skin. "Three little dots, boop boop boop." Linger, soft caress. "It was one of the first things I noticed about you."

She leans away, jaw gone slack. "What?"

"Uh." Sitting next to her, knees touching, feel the divide. Stare at the ground, the grass, the cross, the dirty blonde highlights on the back of someone's head; the nun, the cross, the door, the cross. The cross. "What's with the cross, hmm?"

Amy blinks, still staring.

"They can't really expect us to believe those holes represent each and every one of our sins. I mean seriously think of how many billions of people there are there's just no way—"

"Wait, what?"

"—that they could put all the sins of the whole wide world into one cross that thing would be dust I mean unless they're trying to be historically accurate—"

"Stop."

"What's going on back there?" the nun says.

"—in which case there were less people back then so maybe that'd be a little more feasible butIdon'tknowstillseemsfishyfish!likethecathol icsign!hahaha—"

"Slow down!" Amy whispers. "I can't understand you when you go off with your accent like that."

Heart beating fast, sputter, "I don't have an accent."

She wrinkles her brow.

"I don't have an accent. You do."

She blinks, blinks, lets her brow fall. Both of us staring, nothing to say.

Hearing the heavy clack of shoes advancing, glance up at the wrinkled face shrouded in black.

"Do you have something you would like to share with the class?" the nun asks.

Your religion is logically flawed. "No, miss."

"What's all this chatter back here?" she says, her voice rising.

Turn to Amy, the nun. Nothing to say.

The nun steps back, points to the door on the left. Apologize, accept punishment, blue fabric rustling against skin as faces strain to see. Shoes clacking, the nun leads me to detention.

◆

I wondered how far out we were. The shelf was shallow, white sand peppered grey that sprawled for miles. I'd strain to hear clinking bottles from shore, or someone yelling, or spoons scraping against pots of rice and peas—anything to judge far away we were, like counting thunder.

Sometimes my father would wander out till the cool water rushed up to my chest. Flailing against him, legs kicking, I'd feel his arms abandon my back. So I'd kick faster, faster.

"Exactly," he would say, "now let go."

I wouldn't. I'd lock my arms and clench my eyes and I wouldn't let go. So he would sigh then stand up as he carried me farther out to sea.

◆

Arranged around the room are scented candles melted low, wax bulging around the flames. Prayer room; detention; chance to confess my sins before Christ. Kneeling on the pillow, look up: on the wall, just above eye line—Jesus framed, his hand over his heart. From a hidden speaker, music floats about the room: Gregorian chants in half time; perfect for a nap.

The bell rings. Doors bursting open, yelling and screaming invade the silence. Passing period.

A nun pauses then peers in.

Eyes closed, pretend to repent: dear Catholic God, can you put Protestant God on the line? Apparently you two aren't the same thing, and you think I'm doomed to Hell. *Tsk tsk*, not very benevolent of you.

The nun steps back, seeming satisfied. She walks away.

Shoes squeaking; music droning; what would they do if they came in and saw me napping?

Two columns of shadow streak over my knees. Glance over. It's Amy and Barrett staring in.

"Akua," Amy says.

"Akúa."

"Akua," she says again, slowly, trying so hard to say it just right. She says my name again, and again, "Akua, Akuua," trying to get it but falling short.

Barrett coughs.

Smirking, whisper to him, "You still owe me five dollars. Don't think I've forgotten."

He laughs as lockers start slamming shut. Barrett sprints down the hall; bell's going to ring soon. Amy lingers for a moment. From across the pool of light she looks at me, and waves.

◆

He threw me in. Arms thrashing, trying to steady. He pried my fingers from his neck and threw me in. Struggling upwards, spotted my father, the glare from the sand burning my eyes. Dipped down, kicked harder, came back up. Standing where the water meets the shore he looked at me, and beckoned. Come, come. He carried me out to sea. Come, come. ◆

Joseph Salvatore

FOR THE BATTERING OF HEART IN THE MATTER OF OUR DAUGHTER, THAT SHE MAY RISE AND STAND, O'ERTHROWN BY THEE AND MADE NEW

Dear Lord, we ask that our little girl learn the lines that her mama and I have taught her. Lines that you yourself done spewed on Joseph of Nazareth and on all those who would listen thereafter. Lines that our little girl must memorize to recite for when they put her up in the box. Truth is, we all know it's true, her mama and me. *The spirit comes when it will, upon those ferocious wings.* Says she does too, our little girl. Says she knows it's true. Never one to argue, she. Dutiful little servant. And it's best to believe. Best for us all. Such faith she puts in us, her parents. Such a child of faith and faithful ways, our little girl. Please help her to learn those words, Lord. *She was visited upon.* And that's the fulsome truth, Dear Lord. Yea, that you help her to memorize the truth. We ask this in Your Name. And we did our part. Before they took us. Taught her those words, Dear Lord, said them along with her, again and again, in her little room, watched her small lips purse and pucker, her eyes frightful in their concentration: *visited upon, visited upon, visited upon.* And we put her in her pretty plaid Sunday school dress, in her little pink bedroom, on her bed reading the Bible. We did this immediately after the school called, when they said they were concerned, when they said she was bleeding on her school seat, said we should expect a visit. And, lo, but didn't that visit come soon after that call, the knock on the front door of our raised ranch, that very afternoon, knocked they did, so polite they were. But you know all about it because you know all. You saw it all. You were there, you're always there—everywhere, in my head and in my deeds, in my prayers and intercessions, in the sweat on my sheets, any action on my part already prefigured, a part of your divine plan. Seems to me, now looking back, you might have had some orchestrating role in it all. Something larger than my meager mind could comprehend. Perhaps somewhere in the back of my head, as they say, I was led to act out this role. Programmed by my creator. A willing servant, I. For who but you, after all, understands so well the ways and manner of temptation? That great serpent, he of the whisper and waggle, that blower of breezes that lifts the hem of a pretty plaid Sunday school dress and wafts toward a father's nose the siren scent of unbreached girlhood, he of the false promises, he of the great illusion, the king of lies, the grand seducer, that beast was created by you, after all, Lord. Your fingerprints are all over this family's house. She is our little girl. But she is, in the end, your little girl. And that's what we will say to anyone who will listen: *Visited upon in her sleep.* And yet that fucking pig of South Carolina law enforcement said to his partner:

—*Wait, Ray, they got a name for that, what do they call that? A succubus?*

—*Nah, Mike,* said the other pig, a South Carolina nigger pig, standing up free and proud in his blue shirt sleeves, his muscley arms, dangling his shiny black night stick, shiny like his shiny shaved eggplant head, standing in the doorway of our living room, inside our own home, in front of photos of our little girl. *It's* incubus, *Mike, because the male ghost sticks it "in,"and the female ghost "sucks" it. Get it, "suck"? Think he's talking about an* incubus, *Mike.*

—*Aw, that's nice, Ray, got yourself a pneumonic device there. Well, big guy here can call it whatever he wants. His daughter keeps fucking up her story. Like she's reading a script. Says she bleeds 'cause she got stigmata. You ever heard of a stigmata staining a school seat like that, huh, big guy?*

I said I was going into that bedroom to talk to my little girl and to straighten this all out, and that's when the white pig broke my arm—on purpose, I do believe, Lord. He twisted me around in my own kitchenette and put my wrist behind my back up to my neck, up to where it shouldn't have gone.

—*You're hurting me, officer, sir.*

And I didn't mean to spit, but spit I did, and he pushed my arm higher and the other pig tore my wrist-skin inside too-tight handcuffs, my arms bent back behind me at the elbow and up near my neck like ferocious wings, and then they yanked my arms down the wrong way and that's when I both heard and felt the snap above my right forearm, my pitching arm, that sublime athletic talent you gave me, Lord, gone to rot there with that one snap, that precious bone's break, and now all the poor thing does is hang loose like an empty shirt sleeve, no more fast balls from that one, no sir, Lord; pain beyond my poor power of description. A no-good arm is no good in Broad River.

And lo, would they have dispensed the same treatment and said all that accursedness to Joseph in regards about the Blessed Virgin, Lord?

Her gravid womb, its blessed skin still miraculously intact, the mystery of that *sacred threshold* never breached. Would they have dragged Joseph of Nazareth—he who never breached that *sacred threshold*, he who stood aside for the Immaculate cuckolding—would they have dragged him across the linoleum floor of his own kitchenette on his knees, pulled him up by his hair and ears to his Formica countertop, holding with their South Carolina pig hands his cheek against the dark brown glass of his microwave oven while they took turns striking and again striking the splintering bones of his shins with their polished black clubs, striking him long after he swore he wouldn't try to run again, wouldn't try to kick again, wouldn't spit no more? Would they have done such a thing to me if I was Joseph, O Lord? Tell me, would they have done? Even after I told them at my front door, responding to their polite-as-fuck-all knocking, before they pushed their way in and past me, breaching with their manly intention my own sacred threshold, even after I told them that I was at prayer just now and to excuse me from these legal matters of the world, these accusations wrongly issued? Polite, I was, even after they answered me in the negative when I asked if they had a warrant. Would they have done? *Some mistake made somewhere, officers. I hereby solemnly promise to clear it all up A.S.A.P. My little girl got groined on the cross bar of her bike this weekend, that's all that mess on her seat was. But now that you mention it, officer, as regards what she was saying, we did hear ghostly noises in her bedroom last night. She wouldn't tell us whatall it was about when we came knocking, and we couldn't open the door, try as we might. She must have locked it. And we in this house here, we respect a person's privacy.*

And so we ask, Lord, her mama and me, who want to keep her with us, and us out of harm's way (for you know, as do I, what they do to you in here for this kind of thing), we ask you, nay beseech you, Lord, with all the angels and saints, we ask that our little girl, with the tattered and torn hem of her pretty plaid Sunday school dress, her missing skin, her breached threshold, her immaculate wound, we ask that she learn the lines we taught her. Express and annunciate the mystery of her own breached threshold. We have faith you will help us, Lord, her mama and me. And when I think back to the boy I was with the good pitching arm, those dark days when I questioned not only my talent, but my mind, my very thinking process itself, as I'm sure you recall Ma saying all the time back then: *There's something wrong with the way you think, boy*, she'd say, I'm sure you recall her words, Dear Lord. And, now, when she comes to Broad River for her visit, while I wait in here for an answer to my prayers, she says it again and again, words she seems to have memorized. She sits across from me, the benches cold and hard, the glass smeared with spit and snot, the cameras always on, the guards watching our every fucking move, and all the other visitors smoking 'cept for Ma, her golden Bible in her gingham lap, her hands folded upon that heavy book, her eyes unblinking, she looks through the smeared glass and says, *I'll always come visiting you, boy. But you can't count on me forever. You gotta invite the Lord in. Open yourself to his presence, boy. He the only visitor you ever gonna need. He the light. He the cure. Let him in when he knocks, my son, let him in, and I swear, all the days of your life, you shall surely know peace.* ◆

Christopher Patton

BLUE MOUNTAINS WALKING

Walking forward does not obstruct walking backward.
Walking backward does not obstruct walking forward.
This is called the mountains' flow and
the flowing mountains.
—Eihei Dōgen, "Mountains and Waters Sutra"

1.

Not
to know in what
way not to
go.

Hit by
words a hart
of words
hid

inwards.

2.

As to
history, whirl-
igig, no truth in it just
wound.

Wind has her as trees in its teeth.

Dread pours down on the scene.

3.

Could
you find anyone anywhere
deserved it no.

I saw you with eyes of the all-
body then

beaten, unbeaten.

4.

And been curious awhile how
it'd come to us,
but this.

Rain on rain
come over shining smashed
up distances from

a core of care to cry no

no to
all that
insults your quote soul.

Stephanie Pippin

MARRIAGE

A drop of strawberry jelly on cheap white china—a fertility dream.
I was sixteen. I wanted a baby so bad to settle me down. Friday
night on the back porch after cards. Touching like that in the
darkness, there was so much of us, so much between us, all of it
enormous. He held both my hands. When he left I took them back.
I buried him in myself so he could go on and get out of my mind.
I wish the weather would change. Mornings I walk to work—
grasshoppers roll ahead of me light as wind and I'm almost there
when I hear the Dallas traffic rush like an ocean. The manager
watches me coming. She says he'll make me quit when he gets
out. I think of the girl I was. Sometimes I see her up ahead of me
crossing the field. What she don't know. I'm finished with marriage
and I can't have a baby with Roy or anyone else. I want to tell her
we are already dead. That this is not real. There was once so much
of us but we got buried in the grass. If I met her I'd ask her to make
something happen; I'd ask her to make the winds blow.

GIRL

If I could I would sing
what it's like to be dragged
under such hunger, that
when the lions came their touch
felt like my mother's
and the stink
of their mouths was the stink
of a love so hot it peels
flesh from a body. I felt
no pain, only becoming
one of them: my blood
on their tongues, their eyes
blank as judgment: one of me
for all of them, all my life
lived in that instant
before the lights came to find
what was left of me.

A DREAM

I fall and far. Sometimes I wake full of holes. Then they come
for me with scissors in their mitts and I am a paperdoll Bonnie
for the taking—scraps of my dress for their memory books, my
hair for souvenirs. All those sob-sisters, those magazines.
Everybody wants a piece of me. Like I wrote we are over. I search
the dark for him always his name on my tongue. Even as they
haul me out. I got so I loved him and that's the glue. On quiet
stretches of road at night, nearer my god to thee, we'd slow down
and listen to radio hymns, to the trees going by and the sky was a
vast black water where stars dissolved him and me. Lord leave me
there to wake or not. I can't say where we're headed. We just go—
smoke rising white like parachute silk, like dust down the road.

Lynn Melnick

LANDSCAPE WITH WRITTEN STATEMENT

You wrap my ribs in gauze —
an experiment with the word *tenderly*

after your hands left my throat too bruised to speak.

While winter sun squints at the ghost flower
dying in its shabby terra cotta

far from home

men tell me to be honest about my role in the incident:

Okay, yes
I should have stayed inside

while you railed from the sidewalk

but my confused heart got into the car.

What happened is
I once spent too much time in the desert

so pogonip seems glamorous hung stuck in the trees
like when blood dries on skin

and I want to wear it

out for an evening,
pat my hands over its kinky path down my face

because: fuck you,

you didn't find me here.
I brought you here.

Katie Cortese

WELCOME TO SNOW

My brother Simon, who was doing steroids in the hopes of middle-linebacking his way to fame and fortune, got his high-school girlfriend pregnant just before their senior year. The first week of school, Arlene did two pregnancy tests in the third-floor girl's lav. After both turned up with pink plus signs or blue lines or whatever meant Whoa Nelly, You're in Trouble, she left the boxes in the trash to feed the rumor mill and spent the rest of the day in the nurse's office, complaining of a migraine. By November she was living with us, sleeping on a cot in my room.

Before the baby, Arlene was so thin her hipbones showed. Her hair fell blue-black past her shoulders and she was always busy with a ring to twirl or a belt to cinch or an eyelash to dig out of her eye, so when she took the time to talk to you it made you feel important. This was the year my brother kept inviting her over and then leaving suddenly to take care of "the business," transferring something in a plastic baggie—wisps of green, wisps of white—from his metal tackle box to his pocket and shuffling out the door without a wave.

At those times Arlene was stuck with me. Two years older, she was infinitely cooler than anyone else I knew. We'd hike behind my house—a three-bedroom deal in the shadow of the Bourne Bridge, assaulted by the constant sound of traffic—to where crabgrass met scrub pine. The trash train ran through the woods between us and the Cape Cod Canal. We never went to the scenic bike path. Too many joggers and tourists with strollers, plus the occasional streaker.

Next to Arlene, I was the first to know about the baby. The day she told me, early September something, she was smoking cigarettes and I had a pack of cloves even though Spacey Sputner had claimed at lunch they gave you black lung. Not only had the pack cost ten bucks but I hated Spacey Sputner, who was my only real competition for class valedictorian. That day the bridge above us was quiet in the lull before rush hour.

"Poor Mrs. Ferguson," Arlene said, one foot tapping a second-growth scrub, startling a light rain of needles. I knew she meant the black-and-white dress our Algebra teacher had worn.

I choked on a lungful of sweet-smelling vapor. "Jesus," I said. Arlene and I had math together because I was advanced and she was behind. "She was making me seasick."

When Arlene laughed, my knees hummed and tingled. She had a way of making me forget the loner I normally was. I sent up a prayer that she and Simon would never break up.

The cigarettes were my brother's. Arlene had dug them out of the fetid dark of his sock-smelling room, because, unlike me, and for reasons unknown, she wasn't afraid of him. But she didn't have memories of him as a kid, when he was gentle. Around eighth grade, he'd seen all the other boys poised to fill out like water balloons, and panicked because he had our father's stringy build. When weights weren't enough, he started buying pills, then selling some, among other things. Arlene knew about the steroids. She said he used them safely, in cycles. Freshman Bio told me his voice might get high, and he risked liver cancer, but the only surface effects were bowling-ball biceps, a short fuse, and ugly grunts when he lifted in the basement.

The clove made my lips taste sweet and sad like a brown leaf crushed underfoot. Despite Spacey Sputner's know-it-all claim, I liked them because they were a no-calorie treat. I was set on making my hipbones push through my school skirt like Arlene's. While my father was a classic beanpole, my mother was Rubenesque. I took after her, but I figured if my brother could mold himself into muscle and toughness it was possible for me to go the other way. Arlene showed me yoga moves sometimes, downward-dogging with a lit cigarette between her lips.

In the woods, before Arlene's news shattered the day, I was thinking about Peter Allston, Sacred Heart's personal Tom Brady, and the car ride home. Simon had driven with Arlene in the front, as usual, but the back seat was shoulder-to-shoulder football players. "Peter has lap space," Arlene had said, snapping her gum. He'd blushed, but moved his bag so I could sit.

Peter was an okay quarterback, and cute enough, but weirdly shy. He sometimes stuttered. Simon, on the other hand, was the best middle linebacker Sacred Heart had ever seen. Everyone at school called him "Girth." Despite abysmal grades, he'd been approached by a couple of scouts. The one he liked best was from Ohio State University. I had two more years to perfect my escape plan, which could only involve an academic scholarship. No matter what, I wasn't getting stuck here like my parents, who'd never lived anywhere else.

In the woods, Arlene dragged and let it whoosh out. "I'm pregnant," she said.

A semi screamed over the bridge above us, erasing all thoughts of Peter and his lap under my thighs, the way the bare skin on my legs had come alive from hip to ankle.

"What are you going to do?" I said. Arlene was Catholic, like my family, so I figured she'd keep it, but I couldn't see Simon welcoming a newborn. If he could pull up his grades, he was sure to land a spot on some D-1 institution's elite defensive line next year. I was scared for her, no matter what she decided.

Arlene pinched her cigarette between her fingers, staring at it before grinding it out on the wooden bottom of her clog. It left a black smudge, like a freckle that should be checked for melanoma. I did the same with my clove and we buried our filters in wet leaves.

"What did Simon say?" We walked back, hugging our elbows against the chill. I was glad I hadn't mentioned Peter. What had happened in the car paled before this new disaster.

"He doesn't know yet," she said.

The world acted like teenage pregnancy was no big news. TLC packaged it up to make it seem as entertaining as "The Voice." But I was walking next to a pregnant teen. Inside her was a new life, blind, curled up like a hibernating gerbil, its beating heart the size of a pencil eraser beneath pinkly translucent skin. She lived with her grandparents and two brothers on Cotuit Road. Their mother had checked out years ago, coming back every three years to visit.

"I freaked you out," she said, biting at the skin around a fingernail. "I'm sorry."

When I licked my lips, the clove's sweetness had gone. "Are you guys getting married?"

"I don't want you to worry, okay?" she said. Her face stretched tight when she smiled.

When we emerged from the woods, Simon was smoking in a plastic patio chair, dragging a sneaker against water-stained concrete. Arlene sat on his lap so the chair legs splayed out.

He tossed an empty pack of cigarettes at her chest. "You take some of my smokes?"

She looked down at the pack in her lap. I'd seen him swing at my father for changing the channel from ESPN to PBS. Dad had side-stepped and ordered Simon to take a walk and cool off. In the end, that's what had happened, but I couldn't forget the shape of Simon's fist— big around as a coffee can—cutting a swath through the air. Over one missed double-play.

"What's yours is mine," she said. My heart hollowed out, waiting for him to dump her, baby and all, to the ground. Instead, he took her bottom lip in both of his. She kissed him back.

Peter Allston had nice lips, full and never chapped. I'd never been kissed and could only imagine what it might feel like, though the car ride today had given me some idea.

I slipped into the house through the slider. My mother was making a chicken pot pie.

"Homework done?" she said. I felt bad because of the announcement in her future. We'd been close when I was young, but had drifted apart. Since I was the good one she left me alone.

"I did it during free," I said, thinking it was Simon's grades she should worry over.

In my room, I lay down and closed my eyes until I could feel again Peter's knees fitting neatly into the space behind my own, the vibrations of the uneven road, the two of us jouncing along together. Faintly, I heard Arlene's laugh in the back yard and knew she hadn't told him yet.

Pregnant Sacred Heart girls had to trade uniform skirts for track pants. This was supposedly for comfort but doubled as a scarlet letter. My brother's friends surrounded Arlene like an armed escort when the news got out in mid-September. Boys I knew as The Rickster and Big Dave as well as just plain Peter Allston buffered her from swinging doors, sympathetic teachers with their hands out to cop a feel, frantic freshmen spilling around corners grasping ballpoint pens and compasses like spears.

Peter nodded when I passed him on Arlene duty, but despite being in the same Chemistry class—him in the back, me in the front—we hadn't talked since that day in the car, weeks before. Still, my body was acutely aware of him whenever we were in the same room. In Chem, I'd look back during a lecture on covalent bonds to see him picking his teeth with a paper clip. At football games I watched him freely from the bleachers. I decided the day in the car had been a fluke, the spark our bodies had struck nothing but an accidental, automatic, biological response.

Arlene's transition into our house began slowly. By the first week of October, she was staying for dinner every night, talking brightly and running her silken ponytail through her hand. After dinner sometimes Simon would drive her home. Others, she'd stay and watch TV, picking at her nails on the love seat, offering fashion advice to the Real Housewives of wherever.

Space was tight at her grandparents' place. They had their hands busy with Arlene's brothers, one in eighth grade and one in sixth, who'd been left, like Arlene, when their mother had climbed onto the back of a boyfriend's Harley and split. There was never a decision for Arlene to move in with us, but we had plenty of food on our dining-room table, and she liked the chores I despised, singing Joni Mitchell songs over the vacuum in a brave and wild soprano.

More of her stuff appeared in the house every day, a downy white comforter that spent the day behind the couch, a Teddy bear with hot-pink fur, some books, her toothbrush, her Oxford uniform shirts. The week before Halloween, my mother brought up the green cot from the basement and left it in my room.

The first Tuesday in November, the night before the biggest Chem test of the semester, I came home from school to find Arlene on her cot with a washcloth on her eyes and a pink plastic tub on the floor, empty, beneath her. "Not feeling so well?" I said. Just the effort of lifting her head to look at me sent her coughing and sputtering over the tub.

"I'm sorry," she said, between spasms. I patted her back, sending frantic mental signals to my mother, but no one came.

"It's fine," I said, forcing my teeth to unclench. I wanted to be the kind of person who didn't mind dropping everything to care for her, but I really needed to study. It was dark by the time she slept.

So I wouldn't wake Arlene, I took my book and flash cards to the dining-room table. The flicker of light on the patio brought me to the door and then outside, where my mother sat smoking, encased in a parka lined with fake fur. There was a lit candle on the table, from the hurricane drawer, and a Stieg Larsson book in her hand.

"I don't understand why she can't sleep in with Simon," I said. "What harm could it possibly do now?" My feet on the cold concrete were bare.

"I thought you two were friends," my mother said.

"We are," I said. My stomach turned with disloyalty. She was really my best friend, outside of my books. "She just needs, I don't know, a mother—"

"Maggie," my mother said, steadying a glass of wine she had balanced on her leg. The cigarette jittered almost imperceptibly in her cold fingers. "This wasn't in anyone's plan."

"Are they getting married?" I said. "Is Simon dragging her to East Boondock State?"

"Until he gets his grades up, he's not going anywhere," she said, which wasn't an answer.

I wanted my mother to act like she cared. She and my father had Simon right after high school, which had put all her plans on hold indefinitely. Once, after too many glasses of wine that I kept sneaking sips of, she told me her greatest dream as a little girl was to join the Navy and sail all around the world. After Simon was born, she took a job as a secretary in a nursing home, for the time being, and worked there still, seventeen years later.

"Aren't you disappointed?" I asked.

My mother turned a page. Behind her was the dark window of her bedroom, where my father was asleep already. "What's done is done," she said, ashing over the concrete.

"I can't work. Don't you care about my grades?" A TV from the Parsons' house blared a rerun of the "Tonight Show" and what I really wanted was to fold myself into a parka, pour my own glass of wine, and study by her candle.

"You'll do just fine," my mother said, staring into her glass as if she could read pulverized grape flesh like tea leaves. "You always do."

A barge moaned by in the canal, and I shivered. If it was me who'd gotten pregnant, I wondered if she would be so calm, take so little responsibility. But I was a careful girl. She thought she didn't have to worry about me. I stood out there a minute longer, waiting for her to look up at me, or say good night, squeeze my wrist, smile.

Simon drove us to school early the next morning to meet a new tutor his coach had found. His hand swallowed my elbow before I could get out. "You have Chem with Allston?"

I froze. The day in the car was months ago now, but what if Peter had said something, and now Simon was pissed? Just last July I'd seen my brother put his fist through the kitchen window because my mother told him to stop sneaking beers. "Yeah," I said. "So?"

"Give him this," he said, producing a white envelope from his back pocket. He let go of me then and got out, circling the car to open Arlene's door. I'd never seen him do that before.

Everyone was early to Chem, their noses close to the formulas as if trying to inhale the mysterious combinations of numbers and letters. I was the only sophomore in the class. Otherwise, it was all juniors and a few seniors who'd skipped it last semester, or had failed out. My brother had managed a C+ last year, but a few of his friends were in it now as seniors. Peter Allston had ear buds in so a faint whine of Incubus clung to him like static electricity.

"Here," I said, dropping the envelope on his desk. "From my brother."

"Girth was supposed to give these to me last night, so I had time to look them over," Peter said. There was an empty seat next to him. Though I usually sat in the front, I took it, watching him slide five thin strips of paper covered in writing out of the envelope. He sorted them on his desk, glancing up to make sure Ms. Clemson still hadn't arrived. With a roll of tape from his pocket, Peter attached the first strip to his pencil, showing me how if he cupped his hand right it couldn't be seen. "You probably studied your ass off. Or maybe you don't need to."

It was social suicide to admit to liking school. "I couldn't," I said. "Arlene was sick."

"You took care of her?" he said, looking up. "That's really sweet." I recited molecular formulas to calm my heart. AuBr, gold bromide; CH_3OH, methanol; H_2O, good old water.

"Not really," I said, but Ms. Clemson had come in and my voice was lost in the flurry of last-minute questions.

Though I hadn't had to ride on a lap since that day two months ago, I thought about it almost daily. That afternoon, the Rickster had been up against the far rear window, running his tongue over his lips for a passing pair of freshman girls. Big Dave's big laugh had echoed in the Buick. "Imbeciles," Arlene had said into the mirror, picking lipstick off her teeth. Meanwhile, I sat sideways on Peter's lap. It was cramped. My head had grazed the roof and I'd had to hold Arlene's headrest to stay upright.

Peter shifted me around until his knees were under my knees. "You all in?" he said.

I'd looked back at him, over my shoulder. He had two freckles to the right of his mouth and on his chin a tiny forest of honey-colored bristles. "Yeah," I said, and he'd closed the door.

My shirt billowed loose over my skirt. Peter's fingers played a lefty piano on the side of his knee, twitching my skirt until my legs prickled into goose bumps. Thigh to ankle, their lengths felt unconnected to me, anecdotal, but crackling with possibility.

We were almost to Dave's house, our first stop, before Peter's fingers slid between the bottom of my thigh and the top of his. Slowly, so slowly. I dipped my chin to my right shoulder, looking back at his uptilted face. He stopped, waiting for permission. The other guys were arguing about the greatest running back in the N.F.L., Adrian Peterson or Chris Johnson. They were distracted. Still, it was all-over wrong. My brother was in the car. It was sick, even, but I didn't want him to stop. I tried to nod, giving my okay, and brushed my forehead against Arlene's headrest. She must have felt it because her eyes caught on mine in the side mirror.

I didn't know then she was carrying the burden of those E.P.T. tests. All I knew was Peter's fingers began moving again, inching in and back until one brushed the pilled elastic at the edge of my underwear. He stopped again, as if I might change my mind, but I only gripped Arlene's headrest and shifted a little to the right. That underwear was the oldest pair I owned. He didn't seem to mind.

By then my nerves were high-tension wires, and parts of me were pulsing that had been asleep my whole life. I was still gripping the headrest, eyes closed, holding my breath without meaning to, taken over by the warmth that pooled between us now, and what felt like a delicate gathering of golden fibers drawn to the place Peter's finger was slowly tracing, when Simon jerked to a stop in front of Big Dave's house. "Someone let me out of this deathtrap," Dave said.

I panicked, reaching for the door handle and spilling into the driveway on the verge of something I had only heard about, secondhand, at sleepovers. Peter gasped as I slid off, and followed me into the driveway, turning away from the car, but not before I'd seen the bulge in his jeans. It made me glad to know the warmth had worked both ways.

I waited to be discovered, but all that happened was Big Dave trotted up the path to his house and Peter asked me to grab his backpack. "Think I'll walk home from here," he'd called over his shoulder. He took his bag without touching me. "Sorry," he whispered, jogging away before I could ask if he was sorry he started it, or sorry he didn't finish.

"Our next game is at home," Peter said now, in class, under buzzing fluorescents. I blinked to see our test was rolling toward us as the students in the front each took a sheet and passed it overhead. I focused on the rustling of paper. "You should come, if you want."

"Maybe I'll try to make it," I said, smiling wider than I meant to.

The chain reaction he ignited in me then was as irreversible as the one that had taken place in Arlene's body, even if we didn't make any sense. Peter was a catch. I was medium pretty. He dreamed of the N.F.L. and my heart thrilled to decipher word problems. I tried to see myself as he did, a short girl with dirty-blond hair. Skirt riding high on pale thighs, bare legs in brown loafers. I could only chalk it up to pheromones and the mystery of human preference that Peter—who would never see the beauty I saw in numbers—only had to smile to set part of me aglow.

Ms. Clemson's exams had landed on our desks, each white as the foam atop a wave.

"Good luck," I said, biting my lip, some instinct tilting my head for me.

"Don't need it," he said, winking and twirling his doctored pencil between his fingers.

Even though I finished the test before Peter, I checked and rechecked my answers, waiting to leave until he dropped his test in the pile at the front.

"Brutal," he said in the hallway.

"I'm pretty sure I bombed it," I lied. The hour had flown by for me in a satisfying blur.

Peter nodded. "Me, too. Which sucks. I really need to pull a C."

"Good luck with that," I said, so we could laugh. He was concerned with passing, not excelling. But when I escaped, it wouldn't be because of my explosive forty-yard passes.

"Maggie," he said. We were at the top of a set of stairs, me poised to go down. Girls in plaid and boys in khakis parted and rejoined around us. I stepped closer so only the width of my textbook kept us apart. He pushed a crisp piece of paper into the breast pocket of my Oxford shirt, his fingers lingering there a beat longer than necessary. "Tell Girth thanks for me, okay?"

I nodded, then made myself wait until Algebra to pull out the paper with trembling fingers. It was only the envelope that had held the cheats, blank on both sides, but I remembered the pressure of his fingers and knew what it meant all the same.

My brother used to have a thing for Star Wars. A secret shelf in his closet still holds all the figures he used to collect, little plastic Boba Fetts and Darth Vaders and frog-faced Jabba the Hutts. Star Wars was the thing my brother did with Dad until he hit high school and football practice and blow jobs I wish I hadn't heard rumors about in the janitor's closet. By the time I was a sophomore in high school, the thing he did with my dad was fix stuff in the basement, like the furnace, or a wobbly chair. When they had a project, I brought them down their dinner.

A night in late November, when Arlene had gone to bed early, I took two plates of pork chops and green beans into the sawdust-smelling basement. They had the Patriots on the radio.

"Stellar," my father said when I wedged his plate on a corner of the workbench. My father looked more like a professor than a plumber with his narrow face and owl-eye glasses. My brother outweighed him by fifty pounds of pure muscle. The neighbors might have circulated some mailman jokes, but pictures of them at twelve made them look like twins.

"Your mother never puts enough salt," my father said. "Back in a flash."

In his absence, I took a green bean off my father's plate. It was al dente, the way I like it.

"Careful, Mags, you're filling out," Simon said, jabbing a finger above my belly button.

"It's a green bean, doofus. It has no calories," I said, and he laughed. I couldn't remember how long it had been since we'd joked around. Maybe he was gentling for the baby. "Arlene said you got a B on your history test. Looks like you might graduate after all."

"It's just one test," he said, modest for once. He was on one of the beat-up metal stools, the heels of his Nikes balanced on two different rungs. When I picked up another green bean he picked up one of his own. *"En garde,"* he said and brandished the bean, thrusting until I parried. We'd had light-saber wars in the back yard when we were younger, our battles made dramatic by the whooshing of cars on the bridge above. The current battle ended when he chomped my bean in half. We laughed at the stub between my fingers, and then he plucked that up and ate it, too.

At the home game last Saturday, Arlene and I had sat together, sharing a blanket on the metal bleachers. Peter looked our way once from the field but he didn't seem to see me in the crowd. I'd wanted to tell Arlene that I thought Peter liked me, but didn't want to jinx it. Nothing had really happened yet. She'd spoken first, though. "I barely recognize him out there," she said, and there was no need to ask who she meant. Simon was screaming and beating his chest with fists the size of cantaloupes, hollering into the wind, biceps testing his spandex uniform, veins standing out like tree roots in the reddened flesh of his neck; he was a monster.

"He just gets hyped up for the games," I said, wanting to believe that's all it was.

In the basement, I couldn't forget her eyes widening as if seeing him for the first time.

"You're going have to keep the Hulk away from the baby, you know," I said. My limbs filled immediately with ice. Simon still pinched his green bean. I wondered if I should be afraid.

He twirled the bean between finger and thumb. There was grease under his nails from the lawn mower he and my father had been reassembling before I'd come down. "Come again?"

His empty hand fisted up against his massive leg. Still holding the bean with the other, he stood, looking down on me from the great height of two years and all the inches he'd grown over me. I think I didn't understand until then the way I would always be younger than him. Our father started back down the stairs. I heard him whistling over the thumping of his steps.

"You heard me, Girth," I said, heart rabbiting along. He looked like nobody's father.

"The kid is not your business. Arlene is not your business, and neither am I." He still gripped the bean, green and ridiculously erect, between his right index finger and thumb. He stood and swept the stool against his bench press, where it rang out cheerfully and fell unharmed.

"What's going on?" my father asked, taking the last stairs two at a time.

"Nothing," Simon said. I saw his face go red as a newborn's before he sank into a squat.

"Go on up now, Mags," my father told me quietly, returning the stool to its feet.

"You're scary," I told Simon before I went up, tensing for a blow that never came.

Simon and I made our peace by Christmas, but I still didn't trust him around me or the baby-to-be, due on one of those days steeped in incense and tradition between Palm Sunday and Easter. We all stayed in New Year's Eve, since Arlene couldn't propel herself out of p.j.s.

"Why don't you take the bed instead of the cot from now on?" I said, winding down from a sparkling-cider sugar high. It was snowing small, hard flakes that tinked against my bedroom window. I'd grown to like her presence in the dark. It was like having a sister.

"No thanks, Mags," she'd said. "Maybe when I'm too fat to hoist myself up anymore."

I wondered if Simon's drugs did bad things to their baby. I pictured it pink and healthy, made of springy clean flesh except for the tips of its toes, which were stained a moss green. Or maybe the baby was perfect on the outside, but inside, green fingers busily popped brain cells like soap bubbles. It bothered me that Arlene never seemed to worry. Her placid acceptance was too much like my mother's must have been when Simon's appearance cancelled her best dreams.

We skipped school on Valentine's Day, Arlene and I. It fell on a Friday anyway. My mother just nodded when I told her I felt sick, and Arlene didn't have to say anything. She was big, almost eight months gone, and was always putting my hand on her belly to feel the thing move around. I couldn't believe there was a baby in there. The little kicks felt to me like a bag of rocks set to tumble dry. In the morning, we watched the "Today Show," "Judge Judy," "The Price is Right," and "The Tyra Show," an episode on teenage girls who were trying to get pregnant.

The panelists were twelve to fifteen, or claimed to be. They wore tube tops and mini-skirts, black mascara and too much gel. The girl on the end was thirteen, and sat with her arms crossed the whole time. "I just want something to love me," she told Tyra, tossing straw-colored hair over her shoulder. "You don't know I won't be a good mom."

I was in the kitchen making ramen noodles but I could still hear Tyra promising that after the break G.I. Joseph would yell those girls into shape. I-Want-a-Baby Boot Camp would involve sit-ups and mystery meat and a ban on deodorant for a whole weekend.

"What does boot camp have to do with babies?" I said.

Arlene said, "God only knows. Let's eat outside, I'm burning up."

We took our soup to the glass table on the back patio. It was freezing, piles of dirty snow pushed up against the house and fresh snow coating the seats of our chairs, but we were wrapped in scarves and hats with bobble tops from when Simon and I were kids. The soup streamed white columns that dispersed against the gray sky. I wasn't sure if the cold-and-hot combo was good for the baby, but I figured Arlene would know better than I did.

"Grammy cries every time I go over to visit," Arlene said. "I don't know why I bother."

I slurped my noodles one at a time, wiping hot broth off my nose. "She's still mad?"

"She just keeps saying babies are so expensive, and that I'm in for a hard road."

Grammy was right, I thought, listening to the traffic on Sandwich Road. Someone next door slammed a car door. My parents were footing her bills now, but how long could that go on?

"What do you think of Peter Allston?" I asked. We'd talked every day in Chemistry for months but so far that was all. Arlene drained her bowl.

"He's a doofus. But not bad looking," she said, and winked. Then she struggled to her feet and went inside to put her bowl in the sink. When she got back, my soup was cold.

"I'm dying for a cigarette," Arlene said, rubbing her mittened hands together. It was freezing. Too cold to be outside. Arlene coughed into a mitten. "Are you hot for Peter Allston?"

"Me and a dozen other hopefuls," I said, part of me hoping she'd try and stop me. Say, Be careful, don't turn out like me. Show some fucking feeling, cry a little, tell me she was scared.

Instead she grinned. "Did he feel you up in the car?" Some drops of soup had iced over on the table, so I knew the temperature had dropped suddenly, the way it can in New England, when you least expect it. "I watched you two in the side mirror. The day you sat on his lap."

"The side mirror," I said, nodding. It started snowing again. We looked up at each other and grinned, letting flakes crowd our eyelashes. The surface of my soup filled with tiny ripples.

"This is snow, Baby," Arlene said, mittened hands cupping her belly. It was the first time I'd heard her talk to the kid. She rubbed her middle, looking up, and said: "Welcome to snow."

We finally went inside, because Arlene's lips turned blue around the edges. G.I. Joseph—bald, gap-toothed—was finishing up the boot camp. We put him on mute so we could watch his eyes bug out and his teeth crash up and down. Arlene pretended to calculate the arc of the spit shooting out of his mouth. That was the sort of problem they dealt with in her physics class.

The girls struggled through modified push-ups and cried, cupping their elbows with tiny, soft hands. "They're a bunch of rocket scientists," I said, but Arlene snapped her head up.

"Fucking sad is what they are," she said. "Tyra should give each of them a dog."

We laughed for a while until our laughter turned to tears, and maybe that was what we'd both been waiting for. Arlene said, her eyes streaming, "Fucking Dobermans, man. Great fucking Danes."

We were on the couch and there was no one home but us and she sort of rolled on her side so her head fell into my lap. I combed the snow out of her hair, only it had become a cross between slush and just plain water. Arlene put her face in her hands and barely noticed when I slipped out from under her. When I came back with the hair dryer, she was as still as I'd ever seen her, sobbing with her eyes squinched down into slits. I needed an extension cord from the kitchen before I could switch the hair dryer on. When the hot air hit her face, she opened her eyes.

"It's my hair that's wet, you dumbass," she said, smiling, taking in great gulps of air.

"First things first," I said, and trained the stream on her cheeks, where tears had paved a twisted jungle of mascara paths, alternating right to left so she wouldn't get burned.

My brother joined me on the patio the first Saturday in April. Arlene was laid up on my bed with fake labor pains. The baby would be here in six days, though nobody knew that yet.

"Can I get one of those?" Simon said, lowering himself into a chair.

I tossed him my pack. It smelled like Christmas because of the cloves, but the buds on the trees were a misty green and spring was true to its name, waiting for the right moment to pounce.

"My tutor says my grades are good enough for O.S.U., barely," he said. "I'm going to send Arlene money every month out of my student loans."

"You're still leaving." The cloves' incense smell reminded me that next Sunday was Easter.

He shifted, planting his elbows on his knees. "It was an accident, Mags. They happen."

I took a shallow drag. He was an accident, too. I wonder what it did to him, knowing that.

"I'm sorry," he said. "Is that what you want me to say?"

"Not to me," I said. "Your accident isn't holding me back. Or you, for that matter."

"You want me to be punished," he said, trapping the smoke from his clove in his lungs. It would be dark in there, black, a mine shaft. He shifted in his chair and I was afraid he'd just stand and leave. As a kid, he always dueled as Luke. I was Darth Vader and lost every fight.

"Yes," I said. "No. I just worry about her here, without you. Don't you love her?"

Simon coughed. "I'll come back weekends. I'll just be at school."

"Christmas," I said. "Easter."

"You can take over the business," he said, teasing me. "Make a few extra bucks. The tackle box is all yours." All those baggies folded over harmless-looking pills, herbs, powder.

"Ha, ha," I said, wishing I was a boy so I could hit him and he would know I was serious.

"What do you want from me?" he said. "I haven't done any enhancement for, like, a year. Schools test for that shit. I know I get too angry sometimes, but you act like you hate me now."

There was so much water in the air I felt like someone had squeegeed a sponge over my head. It was too early for humidity but there it was all the same. With one hand, I swept my heavy hair away from my neck. I wasn't sure what I wanted. It wouldn't make sense to take her and a newborn to college, or to marry her quickly before the kid came if that's not what they wanted. We weren't living in the Dark Ages. But I still wanted something, some gesture.

"I just want you to do the right thing," I said.

He came back to the table and reached for another clove, shaking one out for me. "That's the thing, Mags. There is no right thing, not the way you think there is." He stayed long enough for me to have a fantasy that college would fix him. He'd come back a Jedi, my hero again.

In Chem class Friday, the day Arlene's baby was born, Peter told me he'd chosen UMass.

"That's awesome," I said. "Congrats."

I still didn't know if all our flirting was only in my head, but I'd decided to let him sleep with me, if he wanted to, before he left. Just to see what all the fuss was about.

Arlene was five days past her due date and hadn't been in school all week. Peter rode home in the back, behind Simon and me. "She ready to pop yet?" he asked, grinning at no one in particular. I remember looking at him in the rearview, thinking: he is a sweet, dim, beautiful boy.

We were almost home when my brother's phone rang. It was Arlene's grandmother.

"We're at the hospital," I heard her say over the cell, voice crisp and urgent. "Hustle in."

Simon sped the rest of the way. "Get out," he said, his face stricken as if electrocuted.

But—" Peter said as Simon peeled away, stranding him. He'd have a long walk home.

"Come in a minute. No one's here," I said, my pulse quickening so I could feel it in my wrists. I unlocked the house and gave him a tour that ended in my room.

"Neat," he said, eyeing my bed until I had counted every wrinkle in the quilt. We stood there, me crossing and uncrossing my arms and Peter scratching at the grain of his jeans.

"Arlene is having her baby now," I said. If I wanted to propel us into bed it was the wrong thing to say, but to break the tension it was the exact right thing.

"Wanna go for a walk?" he said.

The day was mild, springy, and once we followed the sidewalk into town and escaped the smell of exhaust, Peter reached down and took my hand. We followed the sidewalk past the library and the baseball field behind it. There was a game on. Little boys in purple against little boys in blue. We passed the pharmacy and the pediatric dentist and the bait shop. We passed the graveyard with its markers yellowed by lichen and mold. Peter would find other girls at college. And that was for the best. I think we both knew I wanted to get farther from home than Amherst.

There was a Cumberland Farms on the corner. We went in for ice-cream sandwiches and ate them outside with the curb burning my thighs beneath my school skirt.

Peter licked vanilla off his lips. "I don't know anything about you," he said.

"Okay," I said. I'd eaten my ice cream into a circle. "Sometimes I do yoga in the woods."

He nodded, storing up the information. "That's good," he said. "That's a start."

When his father came to pick him up, Peter kissed me goodbye just as if it had been a real date. His mouth was sweet with ice cream. My brother's message on the machine said Arlene had had a baby girl, seven pounds, three ounces, he was holding her in his arms right now. I pictured her alien-headed as an eggplant, black-haired, strong-willed, blue-eyed, although that would change, the way everything would. There was a brief cry in the background, like proof. ◆

Diane Hoover Bechtler

MEASURES OF WEDDINGS

Date of the wedding—*Saturday October 12, 2000.*
Place of wedding —*Meadow at Opal Lake.*
Colors in the water—*The spectrum.*
Trees surrounding the bridal party—*Hundreds.*
Mixture of guests—*German, Portuguese, American.*
Religion of the bride and groom—*Buddhist with a hint of Animism.*
Weather the day of the wedding—*Perfect 74°F.*
Humidity—*32%.*
Number of Portuguese who complained about the weather—0.
Number of Americans who complained about the weather—0.
Number of Germans who complained about the weather—3.
Number of Germans who blamed the stepmother of the bride for
    not predicting the temperature correctly—3.
Number of Germans dressed wrong—3.
Number of Germans at the wedding—3.
Guests—250.
Guests who arrived by boat—12.
Guests who arrived on horse—0.
Guests who arrived by parachute—0.
Number of chairs—200.
Guests standing—50.
Mosquitoes—*Quite a few.*
Bug spray—*5 cans.*
Relief from mosquitoes—*None.*
Snapshot #1: *The day of his own wedding to his pregnant bride, the
    father of the bride looked at his best man and said, "This is the
    worst day of my life."*
Cost of the wedding dress—$15,000.
Veil—*always.*
Cost of handmade wedding bands—*$12,000 total.*
Bridesmaids—3.
Bridesmaids who watched TV the night before the wedding—0.
Alteration time for the bridesmaid dresses—*4 weeks.*
Groom attendants—*Best man and best woman.*

Total number of parents present—7.

Cost of La Perla bra for stepmother of the bride—$125.

Matching panties—$85.

Pairs of shoes bought by the mother of the bride that didn't match her dress—3.

Color of stepmother's dress—*Navy blue.*

Snapshot #2: *Rats ate the stepmother's carefully stored first wedding bouquet. She buried her second one. A thorny bush grew over it. She didn't carry one at her third wedding.*

Missing—*Grandparents. All dead for years.*

Missing—*Two pets who died the week before the wedding.*

Cost of flying mother of the bridegroom from Portugal—$600.

Cost of translator for the weekend—$400.

Breast implants for the bride—$6,000.

Laser surgery for the mother of the bride—$1,500.

Caps for the stepmother's teeth—$2,000.

Trips to the tanning bed by the stepmother of the bride—10.

Makeup artists for wedding party—2.

Psychotherapy for the stepmother of the bride—$800.

Parties before the wedding—3.

Strippers involved at the bachelor's party—2.

Snapshot #3: *The bride's best friend pulled out her wedding photos after her divorce. They had faded to ghost people. All of them.*

Ceremony length—*25 minutes.*

Path to the altar—*Miles long.*

Snapshot #4: *The bride confided to her maid of honor her dream from the night before the wedding. She had fantastic sex with a gay man.*

Honeymoon length—*10 days.*

Location of honeymoon—*St. Barts.*

Snapshot #5: *Groom's sister collected three engagement rings before she had her one wedding.*

Musicians—*The entire Newboro Symphony Orchestra.*

Number of bells rung—2.

Number of times bells rang—6.

Number of coughs during service—8.

Years bride and groom knew each other before the wedding—14.

Number of pictures taken—*Hundreds.*

Number of poses—44.

Cans on bridal car—32.

One bumper sticker on a truck saying SHIT HAPPENS.

Tranquilizers taken by stepmother of the bride—4.

Number of flower petals—*millions.*

Age of the flower girl—4.

Smiles when the little girl announced she had to "go potty" in the
middle of the vows—250.
Laughing the above caused—*Barrels.*
One loud motorboat passed when vows were being said.
Number of skiers behind that boat—2.
Tears—*Enough to float an ark.*
Joy—*Boundless.*
Groom—*Contemplative.*
Bride—*Radiant.*
Snapshot #7: *Stepmother of the bride learned how to get the German
in-laws to speak English when they are together. She starts speaking
German.*
Carriages transporting guests to the reception—6.
Photos displayed of the weddings of all the parents involved—4.
Size of tent for reception—3,000 *sq. ft.*
Number of trumpets blown at the entry of the bride—4.
Jugglers present—2.
One person in the audience fainted.
Everyone danced.
Glasses of wine drunk by mother of the bride—*Lost track.*
Wallet of the father of the bride—*Empty.*
Parties after the wedding—2.
Pickpockets—*A couple.*
Cars stolen from the parking lot—*1 Porsche.*
Police on the scene—5.
Commotion—*Lots.*
Formula for marriage—*The square root of maybe divided by wishful
thinking.*
Second thoughts—*None.*

Haizi

ME, AS WELL AS THE OTHER WITNESSES

(translated by Nick Kaldis)

hometown stars and flocks of sheep
like streams of white lovely flowing water
run past
a fawn runs past
night's sight in close pursuit

in the vast wilderness, discover the first plant
feet planted in the earth
never to be uprooted
those lonely flowers
are spring's lost lips

for the sake of our days
leave a wound on our face
because there's not another everything bearing witness for us

me and the past
divided by black earth
me and the future
divided by silent air

I plan to sell off everything
people can name their price
other than tinder, tools to make fire
other than eyes

eyes beaten bloody by all of you

one eye set aside for the strewn flowers
one eye never to exit the cast-iron city gates
       black wells

Lori Horvitz

THE BIG SMOKE

After your last relationship with a pathological liar ends, you're a little weary; maybe your vision's gone fuzzy when it comes to recognizing fatal flaws, or maybe you see a little scrap of love at the end of the tunnel and you're willing to do whatever it takes to get it. So when you receive a personal-ad message from a blond Canadian, attractive in that Gwenyth Paltrow kind of way, you write back, not concerned about expensive flights or having to go through passport control to meet her. Right now you are hers and she is yours and you exchange e-mails about what makes you cry, and you say beautiful scenery and thinking about your dead mother and stupid romantic comedies, and she says seeing her students confused, then enlightened, when she teaches them about the social construction of gender. You talk about being a New York Jew, about how you once heard a poet say, "Jews are like everyone else but more so," and she shoots back, "And Wasps are like everyone else but less so." You laugh. Despite the fact that she lives in another country, she's everything you're looking for. You meet on Skype and talk and laugh for three hours. You stare at her lips and imagine kissing them. The next morning, she writes: "I'm a little speechless, so I'll just drink my coffee."

You tell your friend about the Canadian, and she says, "Are you crazy? Canada?" And you say, "She lives in Toronto! It's supposed to be a great city!" You tell your therapist about the Canadian and she says, "Do you think you might have intimacy issues, to seek out women from such a distance?" And you say, "Why limit myself? Besides, I can't seem to meet suitable women in this small town." Your therapist crosses her legs and sighs. She says, "Suitable women come to town all the time." You shake your head from side to side and say, "That's because I invite them."

You and the Canadian e-mail daily and Skype often, but there are nights you don't hear from her. Sometimes you receive an e-mail sent at four or five in the morning. Sometimes she slurs her words and jabbers on. One night she tells you she doesn't live in Toronto; rather, she lives in a small nickel-mining town four hours north. This nugget of information doesn't worry you as much as her drinking. You tell her you can't handle alcoholics, you've already had your share, but she insists she doesn't have a problem. She drinks, she tells you, because she's bored, and it's only secondary to hanging out with friends. She says you shouldn't worry; she stays out drinking all night only two or three times a month. She says she doesn't need to drink, she never drinks alone, and she doesn't like to have drunken sex. She asks you, with a confused look on her face, "What's your definition of an alcoholic?" You don't answer. You're pretty sure she's not telling you the whole truth, but maybe there's not much to do in her small town. Maybe this is what Canadians do. At this point, she's feeding you something you need, scraps of attention, scraps of hope, and the more scraps she throws, the more you want.

You fly up to Toronto, four hours south of the nickel-mining town where the Canadian lives. She meets you at the airport, and she holds your hand while leading you to her car. You like holding her hand. She looks a bit older in person and you think to yourself, probably from all the drinking, or maybe too many hours in the sun, but you quickly get over the wrinkles and kiss her in your Toronto hotel room, and for the next three days, you stroll arm in arm, eat fancy dinners, and take nighttime walks on the beach. You notice that every chance she can, she works on a crossword puzzle, or solving a Sudoku, which she refers to as her other girlfriend. You notice she doesn't look you in the eye when she talks, that she has a tendency to zone out, like your mother.

She orders a few beers at dinner the first two nights, and on the third, you both drink two martinis. You say, "It's getting late, we need to eat." She says, "I could drink all night. I don't need to eat."

After you return home, you have plans to talk on the phone, but she doesn't answer. Two hours later, she calls. She's drunk. It's only courteous to show up for a phone date, you say, especially after spending three days together. She says you should be glad she called at all. You say you don't know if you can do this. You say you feel disrespected. The next day she apologizes, says she will be a better girlfriend. "Have faith in me," she says. "Give me time."

You give her time. After all, she was at a friend's birthday party. But really, you've been through this before.

She visits you in Asheville for six days, and for the duration, she has an awful cold. Still, you tour the Biltmore House and hike the Blue Ridge Mountains. While she lies in bed, a stack of tissues by her head, you ask if she wants an old pair of your Doc Martens.

"Sure," she says, raising her foot. "Put one on and see if it fits."

It fits perfectly.

"It's like the lesbian Cinderella!" she says.

But you're not sure you're her lesbian prince, especially after you go off to teach a night class and she stays home to prepare a spinach pie. When you return, she says she hasn't eaten anything. You think you might smell alcohol on her breath, but you chalk it up to cough medicine. Later you discover four empty beer bottles in your kitchen pantry.

You both agree the trip went well. "Considering how sick I was," she says, "you really were a good sport." She invites you to spend your winter break in her nickel-mining town. You accept.

But before meeting again, she tells you she ignored a student who came to her office to complain about a grade. She tells you she screamed at a workman, called him an idiot and told him to get the hell out. She tells you no one she met on the Internet lasted more than a week at her house.

Your therapist says, "Do you really think you'll escape her wrath?"

"Maybe I should cancel my trip," you say.

"I can see you've already made up your mind," your therapist says. "So have fun. Take notes."

You suspect it's a bad idea to go, but you still hold onto a tiny shred of hope. Maybe she won't need to drink if she's not bored, and, of course, she won't be bored with you around. Besides, you need to play this out, finish the story you started. So you travel to her nickel-mining town in the dead of winter. The roads are icy, the sky gray, and the Canadian points out the city's claim to fame, the Super Stack, the tallest chimney in the Western hemisphere. "We call it 'the Big Cigarette,' or 'the Big Smoke,'" she says. It never takes long to spot the Super Stack, tall as the Empire State Building, looming above the city, dispersing sulfur gases and other by-products of the smelting process.

The Canadian makes homemade desserts and soups and you spend a lot of time in bed and joke about the book you plan to write together about Internet dating. "We'll reënact profile poses," she says. "Ya know, those shots with people on the phone or standing by their sports car." And you say, "How about a caption of: 'I'm at home in a baseball cap or a burka?'"

So far so good, but on the fourth night, she drinks and drinks and drinks. You watch in disbelief, as she drinks one quart of beer after another. You really don't want to keep track but you notice four, or was it five, empty quart bottles lined up. You don't understand how it's physically possible to drink that much. At least she's a happy drunk. She looks you in the eye. She holds her hand out and you dance, and she likes that you dance and says, "How fun you are! A whole other side I didn't know about!" Another night she drinks beer and champagne and whiskey and more beer and she professes her love to you, says why don't we get married, after all, gay marriage is legal in Canada, but soon after, she passes out. You imagine your wedding reception, an open bar at the local tavern, adjacent to the Super Stack. Later she wakes up, makes pasta in the nude, and passes out again. You ask if she remembers the night. She says, "Don't remember a thing. Tell me about it."

You help her slice apples for a pie, homemade crust and all. Her cat purrs and rubs against your leg, and for a moment, you ignore the drinking and imagine making a life with the Canadian. She even stops what she's doing, washes her hands and wraps her arms around you from behind. She kisses your neck, says, "I'm so glad you're here."

To make the piecrust, she uses animal lard, and you pick up the package and say in a joking manner, "It's the poor man's butter." She continues to knead the dough but doesn't say much. Then she accuses you of demoralizing her. "There are consequences to language!" she says. You're not sure how the butter comment is demoralizing, or how language has consequences in regards to pie ingredients. Maybe it's a class issue, but the Canadian grew up solidly middle-class, like yourself.

On New Year's Eve, you stay at the Holiday Inn, a getaway for the night. When you pull into the parking lot, you say, "Maybe we can ask for a top floor, for a quiet room." She snaps back, "What else do you want?" What you want is to ask about language and its consequences, but you keep your mouth shut. Once in the room, she pulls out a crossword puzzle. You take a walk in the bitter cold, past icy parking lots and crowded liquor stores. The Super Stack spews out a purplish-yellow mist. You walk and walk until your nose and cheeks and fingers are frozen, until your lips are blue.

She invites you under the covers, and you watch "The Secret." There's something to this, you both say, then you both make lists of what you want. She wants someone to offer her a great job without applying for it. "I've always gotten what I've wanted," she says. You say you want to get your book published but don't say what's first on your list: finding a healthy partner, one who is able to look you in the eye when sober.

The next day, she accuses you of demoralizing her when you ask if she needs her wallet that's sitting on the kitchen table, before you leave to see a film. "If I needed it I'd take it," she barks. "There are consequences to language." You're not sure how asking if she needs her wallet is demoralizing, but you apologize for any misunderstanding. You think about leaving. You think maybe she's off her rocker. You think about taking another walk around the block when you return from the movie, but it's fifteen degrees below zero.

You make it through ten of the planned twelve days in this nickel-mining town, where pink granite mountaintops have been stained charcoal black. You make it through the Canadian lashing out several more times, and following each incident, she says, "There are consequences to language."

The last time, you respond, "There are consequences to language!" You change your plane ticket. You put on layer after layer of clothing and storm outside at night, not concerned about subzero temperatures. You tromp along the street's edges, slipping and sliding, away from snowbanks and barreling plows, your face and fingers numbed, the Super Stack now a shadowy gash against the black sky.

You could have predicted all of this before you arrived; you knew the end of the story before it began, but perhaps you needed to get the details right. ◆

Alamgir Hashmi

EAST RIVER

Across Carl Schurz Park,
beyond Hoop Garden sloping the other way,
is the telltale riverbank. Daylight,

I pick this walk through the dahlias,
trying to forget who fought here,
and when, to what purpose:

East River's among the most honest,

and impish, it flows in one direction mornings,
another for afternoons.
No source as such; just water at the ends.

I would like to be its temperament.
At six in the evening, children play ball
with their dog; a woman jogs far into the sunset.

Seth Brady Tucker

COLD IS COLD EVERYWHERE

(*for the Lynch family*)

It came to me during patrol, in a bitter
wind, my hands frozen to my 50 cal,
that the cold of wind here in Afghanistan
is the same as the cold in Anchorage,

and no matter where I go, the cold will
be the same, so everything will be the same.
Even in Jacksonville, where I will walk off
a C-141 transport and into your arms. Kyiersta

will be talking now, and maybe she will
know my name this time, not like before,
when she screamed in terror every time
I picked her up. To think the wild heat

of her rage was conceived so passionately
on the icy floor of Dad's cabin, that frigid night
before our wedding! The chill light of Alaska
illuminated our promises to one another

even though we didn't know anything
at all—didn't even know that Kyiersta would
come while I was in boot camp, didn't know
the sound a teenager makes when under

the tracks of a Bradley, didn't know blood
smells like feces when it spoils, didn't know
that from here on out, mail would come
to me already opened. But there are things

I know now, things I will attempt to explain
after it is all over, because you can't begin
to understand that the pain will be enough
to protect our family, even though it will probably

hurt so much to see me pull the trigger,
but please understand that a small amount
of hard suffering now will save us all from a lifetime
of pain, so please, think of it as removing

your gloves and boots and coat, then warming
yourself by a fire that I have built for everyone.

Andrew Ladd

THIS SOLITARY ISLAND

It wasn't until Nathan left the airport, dusk settling, that the first twinge of recognition hit. Not because of the building itself, a modest low-rise ringed by dense histograms of pines, or the countless cabs and buses clogging the road out front; not because of the thousands of other stranded travelers—the crowds milling around the exits, and the curbside, and the grassy median opposite the terminal—and not because of the white, rust-stained cab where he sat with his wife, Paula, both of them too overwhelmed to speak. No: it was the small, blistering decal on the cab window that did it. *Welcome to Halifax,* it said—*Canada's Maritime Capital.* And that, finally, though he'd never been to Halifax or even Nova Scotia, stirred a nagging sense that he'd known something about this place, once. That perhaps he still should.

The answer wouldn't come to him, though, would surface only the next morning, like a word dredged up hours after needing it, and in the taxi he simply settled into his seat to watch, dazed, as their peculiar northern confines slipped by outside: empty malls, and towering lonely billboards; endless clapboard suburbs, the pastel-painted houses collecting dirt in their joints. The pink-edged September sky, revealing nothing.

They'd been on their way home that morning, on a packed 747 from London to Boston, when the flight had been mysteriously diverted. *We're getting slowed down by some pretty strong headwinds here, folks,* the captain had said, any quiver in his voice masked by the P.A. system's hum, *and to be on the safe side we're going to set down in Canada for some extra fuel.* There were groans up and down the aisle. A pause from the speakers. *But there's nothing to worry about,* the captain added, at last; *we'll have you back on your way again in no time.*

There was something unconvincing in that explanation, though, something too eager to reassure, and an anxious murmur had spread throughout the cabin. In front of Paula and Nathan a man explained to no one in particular that in fifteen years of flying he'd never made an unplanned stop like this. Had never even heard of such a thing. *It has to be more than headwinds,* he'd said, nodding, when the woman next to him looked up. *Something must be wrong.* And something was—but it was only once they'd landed, once they'd taxied past the rows of other planes on the adjacent runway, once the engines had spun down and they were sitting, silent, on the tarmac, that the captain told them: *There's been a terrorist attack in New York.*

Nathan's first thought, then, had been his daughter; his first emotion, relief. Bea had turned down a place at N.Y.U. that fall to stay in Boston. She was safe at home. And though Paula hadn't brought her cell phone, a clunker from her office that wouldn't have worked in Europe anyway, and though the satellite phone on the seat in front of them was dead when Nathan tried it—though they had no way to get in touch with Bea whatsoever—he kept that idea of Boston in his mind, the Charles, tranquil, and miles from any trouble, and let it calm him as they waited for more news.

The more he tried not to worry about Bea, though, on this day when he actually had good reason to, the sillier he felt—because even without reason he'd done little else for weeks. Months. Ever since Paula had sold him on the trip to London, piggy-backed on a conference her firm was sending her to the week of Bea's orientation, he'd been unable to shake the feeling that waltzing off for a bourgeois vacation while his daughter made the biggest transition of her life was a lapse, somehow. A repudiation of their closeness.

He'd said all this to Paula, or something similar. Probably he'd left out the word "closeness," and certainly he'd left out "bourgeois"; drawing unfavorable contrasts between her high-powered job as an efficiency consultant and his freelance work, career counselling at local two-year colleges, was something he only did when he was trying to piss her off. But she'd scoffed at his worries, much as he'd expected: her attitude towards their daughter, as with most things, was always more practical than tender. It wasn't as if Bea were moving across the country, she reminded him. It wasn't as if they wouldn't be there for her whole first year of college. *Besides*, she'd added, rolling her eyes. *She's so stubborn, she wouldn't let us help even if we did stay.*

That sort of comment was also typical of Paula's attitude towards their daughter, though here Bea wasn't much better. *Oh, go to London and let her have her way*, she'd told him, also rolling her eyes, on a Sunday walk along the same stretch of river he was now trying to imagine. *You know you'll give in eventually—save yourself some nagging.* She'd looked at him solemnly. *It's sweet you're worried, Dad, but I'll be fine. Really.*

What a change, he'd thought, from even a few years earlier! He remembered an evening when she was fifteen, while Paula was away on business, and his subway home had broken down one night—and when finally he made it back, half an hour late, he'd found a note on the door and Bea, eyes red, waiting with a neighbor. *I didn't know where you were*, she'd sniffed, the two of them walking across their front lawn afterwards. *I thought you might have died.*

He'd been shocked at her extreme reaction, especially at this minor episode—the students he met at work, some only two or three years older, had been through much more and seemed none the worse for it—and so perhaps his response hadn't sounded as supportive as he'd meant it. *Oh, sweetie*, he'd said, *you shouldn't get yourself so worked up. You're capable of taking care of yourself!* Embarrassed, she'd looked at the ground, and that, he'd realized, might explain her insistence he go to London: it was a declaration that she'd changed, that she could cope on her own—and he'd agreed to go, in the end, even if he hadn't told her as much, to give her the chance to prove it. If only he'd known how much she'd have to cope with.

Eventually they were herded off the plane and into a makeshift holding area, a cavernous departure lounge filled to capacity. Across a few rows of chairs, and huddled in circles on the floor, and sitting against the room's walls and giant windows, hundreds sat glassy-eyed and haggard—waiting to be seen, by one of the volunteers bustling around and handing out bottled water, or at a bank of folding tables by the exit, where more staff were processing the crowd.

They sought out a pay phone to call Bea but found twenty others waiting, the line barely moving, and after fifteen minutes they drifted towards a nearby bar instead. A small television there had attracted a news-feed vigil, which they joined, squeezed in between two ashen-faced men in Yankees hats, as that awful, inexorable filmstrip played in endless repetition: collision, collapse, collapse. Collision, collapse, collapse. *It's unbelievable*, one of the men whispered, shaking his head as if the television were somehow responsible.

Paula and Nathan were silent for a while, riveted by the unfolding story, but once the link with Boston flashed on screen—those two flight numbers, destinations points national, origins both the same—they were thrown once more into panic. Nathan couldn't say why it mattered, really, even as he and Paula returned to the phone and pled their way to the front of the line: there was still no chance Bea had been hurt, still no chance she'd been on one of the planes. But Boston's role in the attacks had left it tainted, somehow, had brushed away Nathan's Charles tableau and replaced it with something grimmer: the terminal curbside that morning, the hijackers arriving. Each of them passing through security, staring serenely straight ahead. And all of them sitting at the gate after that, on the dusty leather seats Nathan had sat on so many times himself—a *Globe* folded over one man's knee, perhaps, or an orange juice, bottle damp with condensation, tilting precariously on another's—until finally they were just a row of silhouettes, shrinking forever down the jetway's glowing mouth.

He thought again of Bea, too, of how she must feel knowing those men had been in Boston. Knowing there might still be more of them. He and Paula had left her a credit card for emergencies, and he worried now that in a panic she might have taken it, and the car, and tried to leave town—Paula's brother lived in northern New Hampshire, and two of Bea's best friends had just moved to Georgetown, and he could imagine her deciding to run to them for comfort. Could imagine her snarled in traffic on the interstate, or speeding north along the back roads—or worse, in a wreck, miles from help and impossible to find.

Suddenly, Paula was tugging on his sleeve, covering the phone's mouthpiece with her other hand and telling him she'd gotten through to the operator. For a moment he relaxed: they were going to talk to her. Make sure she was okay. He squeezed Paula's arm and prayed a silent thanks, but soon his wife's face had curled into a frown and his brief composure evaporated.

"No answer!" Her voice jumped a few octaves. "What do you mean, *no answer?*"

Nathan squeezed her arm again, tighter this time, while she barked down the phone to try their Cambridge home instead.

Again, no answer.

Next they tried the uncle in New Hampshire, and then Nathan's brother in Connecticut—but Bea hadn't been in touch with either of them. Even their neighbor, herself in tears over a relative in New York she couldn't reach, said Bea hadn't been home all week. Frustrated, Paula slammed down the handset. "Where *is* she?"

Nathan swallowed, picturing his daughter in a highway ditch. "I—I'm sure she's fine."

"Oh, so am I!" Her eyes were smouldering. "I just can't believe she'd go out on a day like this—as if we wouldn't be trying to get in touch!"

"Come on, now," he said, looking at his watch. "She probably went for lunch or something. What's she supposed to do, sit by the phone all day and wait for our call? She doesn't even know where we are—she's probably worried about us."

Paula clenched her jaw. "It's just so goddam typical of her, Nathan! Showing no thought for anyone else!"

He bristled at that, but before the argument could escalate a member of staff had interrupted, directing them to join the line for the folding tables across the room. Instead Nathan simply repeated that he was sure there was a reasonable explanation, even as his stomach continued to churn, and they made their way towards the makeshift counter in silence.

The exhausted woman they talked to there told them all flights had been grounded until at least the next day, and that while they waited they had a choice of staying at the airport or taking their chances where the authorities were setting up emergency shelters; most of the school gymnasiums nearby would be taking people, she said, and several local families had agreed to house the overflow. Either that or they could try for a hotel, though she did her best to dissuade them: it was only the high-end ones that had space left—she nodded gravely, as if money ought to be their primary concern—and it would be harder to get back to the airport in a hurry if they went all the way to the city. But Paula, still worked up, refused to sleep *on a drafty high school floor somewhere*, and the other woman, lacking the energy to argue, gave them the number for a place downtown. They got the last room.

It was late but still twilight when they reached the city, a modest clutch of stone skyscrapers that again gave Nathan a vague feeling of déjà vu. As they approached their hotel the traffic slowed to a creep, and half a block away stopped altogether—so Paula had the driver let them out where they were and they walked the last few hundred yards, Nathan carrying the luggage.

Inside, the lobby was just as gridlocked. Guests sprawled everywhere—on the overstuffed sofas, and the checkerboard marble floor, and even on a few mahogany coffee tables—and all eyes were fixed on the big-screen television still replaying that footage at one end of the room. Paula and Nathan pushed to the front desk to check in and then hurried upstairs to make another call to Bea, but again there was no answer—so they left her a series of messages to call them at the hotel and, at last, the restaurant downstairs packed and room service running a two-hour wait, ventured out along the main drag in search of dinner. They passed a Starbucks, and a McDonalds, and a few pubs and pizza places with an hour's wait each, but after that the commercial stretch abruptly seemed to end, capped off by a municipal library and a towering golem of Winston Churchill, and they were forced to retrace their steps; they ended up at the McDonald's after all.

There was a line almost out the door—more diverted Americans, Nathan assumed—and while they waited he gazed groggily around him, succumbing to some combination of jetlag and shock. He remembered the last time he'd been to a McDonald's, one of the only times, really, more than a decade earlier: the chain had been giving away a special toy to tie in with Disney's new Little Mermaid movie and Bea, five or six at the time, had practically threatened hunger strike if she wasn't allowed one. He'd relented, but two weeks later the stupid thing's arm had snapped off and Bea had been inconsolable—wailing on the living room floor until Nathan, in a moment of inspiration, had scooped her up and taken her to the library, to borrow a copy of the original Hans

Christian Andersen fairy tale. They'd sat down to read it immediately, in the parking lot, and as her mood had improved he remembered marvelling at how so subtle a choice, to bring her here, had made this tangible difference. He'd wondered if that was good parenting, if it went beyond the things he'd always assumed were necessary, the deliberate things Paula insisted on—bedtime stories, and taking Bea to museums, and enrolling her in art and dance classes. If instead it was at the level of each interaction—each crisis handled—where he could change her fate the most.

He rubbed his eyes, now, worrying again about how she might be coping with the day's events, and where she was, and if they ought to be doing more to find her. And then the cashier was asking for his order and, flustered, he blurted out the first thing that came to mind.

"A *Happy Meal?*" Paula whispered, once the man had turned to fetch it.

He shrugged sheepishly.

There were no empty tables, so once they had their food they squeezed into a booth next to another middle-aged couple. The woman introduced herself as Mary and volunteered, in a way that suggested she'd already had the same conversation several times, that she and her husband, Bob, had been coming home from a long weekend in Paris. She stuffed some fries in her mouth. "What about you?"

"London," said Paula. "Part vacation, part business."

"How great!" Mary beamed. "We went there last year and totally loved it!"

Paula smiled and began to explain where they'd been staying, the two of them easing into cheerful small talk about finding travel bargains, while Bob turned to Nathan to ask about his picks for the World Series. Nathan, though, finding himself irritated by such pleasantries in their current circumstances, gave gruff, one-word responses and barely listened, alternating instead between his worries about Bea and his struggle to work out why Halifax seemed so familiar. His Little Mermaid memory had brought the feeling to the surface again; had given the answer some faint new contour, like the outline of a piece in a darkened room. And yet no matter how he flailed he couldn't quite bring it into reach.

Soon, the food mostly finished, Bob—who had long abandoned the World Series conversation—guffawed at something Mary said, breaking Nathan from his reverie. Still annoyed at their high spirits, he abruptly wriggled from the booth, balling up his burger wrapper and brushing the crumbs from his coat. "Let's go," he said to Paula. "I'm half asleep."

They all stared at him, surprised by the interruption, and cheeks flushing he added that they needed to try Bea again, too. After a few seconds, Paula muttered that he was probably right, and as she stood up and they all said their goodbyes, Mary pushed the box from Nathan's Happy Meal across the table. "Don't forget your toy," she said with a grin, pulling out a bug-eyed plastic doll. He looked at it for a second, not sure how to respond—and before he could, the other three had burst out laughing.

H e slept fitfully and woke to the first drip of sunshine through the curtains. Raising himself onto one elbow—carefully, so as not to wake Paula—he peered at the alarm clock on her side of the bed, its red numbers showing a few minutes before five. He yawned. When they'd arrived the hotel clerk had said there'd be a special breakfast buffet for stranded travelers this morning, but not for another hour—so Nathan lay down again and stared at the television, its screen blank at last.

They had not, in fact, tried Bea again the night before. "Ugh," Paula had said, glancing at the clock as she'd checked the bedside phone for messages. "It's almost midnight. Where could she be?" She replaced the handset and flopped backwards onto the mattress. "Six days on her own and already it's like we don't exist."

"I told you," said Nathan, taking off his watch and placing it on the dresser. "She's probably gone to a friend's place, or the movies or something. Would you want to be trapped in some strange new room on your own right now?"

Paula rolled her head sideways and stared at him. "No, I wouldn't. But after you stormed out of McDonald's I didn't have much choice."

He made a face. "You didn't actually want to stay and carry on that inane conversation, did you? For God's sake, we're in the middle of a tragedy!"

"No, Nathan, we're in the middle of Nova Scotia. We're fine. Bea, as you keep condescendingly telling me, is probably fine." She looked at the ceiling again. "And what happened today is awful, you're right, but we were lucky. We escaped the worst of it. Why shouldn't we be happy?"

He shook his head. "That's a pretty selfish way to look at it."

"I don't give a shit! You sit and brood if you like. I'm going to stay positive." She closed her eyes. "So. Do you want to call her or should I?"

He glanced at the phone. He did still want to talk to Bea, to find out for certain she was okay, to reassure her—but he doubted he was in the right frame of mind for that, even if she answered. Besides, they'd left messages for her everywhere: at home, at her room, at her dorm's front desk, with the neighbors. If she'd come home she would have called already.

"Let's wait till morning," he said, at last, trying to ignore his resurgent thoughts of her dead in a ditch somewhere. "It's late. We're tired.

I'm sure she'll call us if she needs anything."

"Fine," said Paula, and they went to bed.

Now he wondered if that had been the right decision. Shouldn't they have tried her again, anyway? Called the campus police if still she hadn't answered—the city police, even—and reported her missing? Of course, college students were often out at odd hours, and he'd dealt with enough overbearing parents at his job to know he didn't want to be one—but given the circumstances he chided himself for having backed off before they even knew she was okay.

The longer he lay there, though, watching the sun brighten behind the curtains, the more he realized that his daughter being hurt or upset wasn't what scared him. That his fear now—and the fear he'd felt about going to London, actually, if he thought about it—wasn't that she wouldn't cope without him, but that she would. Without realizing it, over the past few years, as she'd filled her schedule with college-app extracurriculars and evenings out with friends, he'd begun to miss the little girl who depended on him. The person who noticed when he was late coming home. *She'll call us if she needs anything*, he'd said the night before. So did her lack of contact mean she didn't? Had she outgrown him already, even with all that was going on?

After a few more minutes, Paula stirred, and by the time six o'clock arrived they were both up and dressed, mechanical apologies made for squabbling the night before. They descended to the lobby, expecting to find it empty, but nothing seemed to have changed since the previous day—as if a new shift of guests had arrived, sometime after midnight, and seamlessly taken over. The faces today were a little blearier, maybe, the rumpled airplane clothes replaced with undershirts or hotel bathrobes, but still the bodies were draped over every seat and surface. Still all eyes were glued to the nearest screen.

Their plan had been to eat quickly and return to the room, to wait for news from the airport and try Bea again once it was later. But as they sat downstairs, surrounded by so many other stranded travelers and the endless news show panoramas of the aftermath in Manhattan, the hotel felt claustrophobic, suddenly, unbearable, and after breakfast they went for a walk instead. There were some public gardens opposite the hotel that Paula wanted to check out, a genteel city block of landscaped lawns and hillocks, and once they'd strolled around there for an hour they retraced the route they'd taken the night before—past the bars and shops, past the glowering Churchill, and on into the downtown core. Everywhere they spotted more captive visitors, floating around the oceanfront like an army of lost souls: single men, gaping at the red sandstone of city hall; groups of young women, chatting as they climbed the hill to the town's imposing Citadel; and parents, pointing out ships across the harbor to their children.

On a winding road along the water they found a small museum of local history just opening for the day, and Nathan suggested they take a look inside. If they could kill half an hour here, he said to Paula, it would be almost nine in Boston when they got back to the hotel—an acceptable time to call, even for a college student—and when she didn't object they paid the modest admission and wandered in. It was full of the usual tourist-trap displays—the city had the oldest surviving lighthouse in North America, they read, and was the birthplace of a Canadian prime minister—but Nathan found himself most captivated by the stranger trivia: the salt fogs that plagued the area, licking in off the sea and eating through power lines; the story of when local police arrested Leon Trotsky as he passed through during World War One. And then what seemed to be the place's biggest claim to fame: the Halifax Explosion.

In 1917, a series of panels explained, a munitions freighter had collided with another boat in the harbor narrows, and in the ensuing fire its cargo erupted—a thunderous blast that flattened half the city. Nathan grimaced as he read the eyewitness accounts of that morning: the dust and metal that had fallen from the sky, the countless firemen who'd perished helping. The people flung through windows by the shock wave. And he thought, too, of that grainy footage from the day before, the towers tumbling and charcoal clouds sweeping through the streets. Even with no television in sight, he seemed fated to carry on confronting it.

Next to him, Paula suggested they move on, but still he lingered by two panels about Boston. Their hometown had mounted the biggest aid effort after the explosion, he read, hundreds of its doctors and nurses traveling for thirty hours straight to lend a hand—and to this day, in appreciation, Halifax provided Boston with its official Christmas tree each year. Nathan thought of all the lightings he'd gone to with Bea, all the *Globe* stories he'd read about those trees, and wondered if that might be why his memory kept circling around this city. But still the unsatisfied feeling was there, as insistent as ever, and only once they'd moved upstairs, into the museum's largest exhibit, a detailed description of the Titanic's last hours, did he finally make the connection. Of course.

When Bea was fourteen, she'd been obsessed with the Titanic, or, more to the point, with the recent movie and its charming, boyish star. Nathan, trying to channel that obsession into something more productive—trying, perhaps, to relive his past glories—had taken her to the library again one weekend, to find some academic sources about the ship and its sinking. Though she'd been dubious at first, she was soon totally absorbed, borrowing as many books as she was allowed, spending the afternoon reading on the couch, and then bombarding him and

Paula all through dinner with each new fact she'd learned—including that the ship's remains had been taken to Halifax. And that, he guessed, was why the place kept niggling: because she'd asked him where in Canada the town was, exactly, and he hadn't been sure. Hadn't been able, for the first time he could think of, to answer one of her questions. Instead he'd shifted uncomfortably, while Paula suggested she look it up in the CD-ROM encyclopaedia they'd bought her for Christmas. *Okay*, she'd said, puzzled, *I will*—and later had brought him upstairs to read the entry. Had asked him what "maritime" meant. Had shown him the few pictures of the city that now made it look so familiar.

He reminded her about it when he talked to her later that morning, at last, perched on his hotel bed and nervously twisting the phone cord around his finger, while on television police stormed the place in Boston where the hijackers had stayed. "Huh," she said, "what a weird coincidence," just as unflappably as when she'd told him, at the start of their conversation, that everything was fine—that she wasn't upset or scared or any of the other things he'd worried she might be. Even when he'd pressed her, when he'd insisted it was okay to ask for help in a time like this, she had insisted with equal firmness that she didn't need any. "It's my first week of college, Dad," she said. "I just want to enjoy it."

"Okay, sweetie." He sighed. "Sorry." Next to him, Paula sighed too. "I'm worried about you, that's all."

"Well don't be," she told him. "I have to go, okay? I need to get to class."

Later he would think back to that conversation—much later, after Bea's freshman year, and her post-graduation malaise, and her eventual move to Seattle for her fiancé—and ask himself whether such cool composure had been for the best. Before long she was acting as if *nothing* could upset her, not the poor grades he knew she was earning, not her inability to find summer jobs, not the series of boyfriends she brought home out of nowhere and who just as quickly disappeared. It was as if she had no emotional responses whatsoever—except that then he would catch her, in their occasional hours together, with tears in her eyes or her breath caught in her throat at little more than a Hollywood disaster film, or the cheering in the streets after a crucial Red Sox win. Almost any suggestion of community spirit, in fact, of people coming together, whether in adversity or triumph, was enough to crack that impassive veneer, and each time it happened he would wonder if it were some legacy of her early refusal to acknowledge anything the matter. Would wonder, worse, if the attacks alone had caused it or if, somehow, it was him. If he could have done something more to prevent her coming out of it so damaged.

That morning in the hotel, though, he lay back on the bed, smiling, and simply let himself be glad she was okay. Suddenly her growing independence didn't strike him as something he ought to worry about. Instead it seemed that her readiness for change as college loomed, for a rupture from the ordinary, had made her see the attacks as less disaster than another difference to which she needed to adjust—and that attitude would do more to help her through the coming weeks, he was sure, than any words of comfort he could have offered.

So instead of fretting any more, or giving into the news as Paula had beside him, he closed his eyes and tuned out the television and finally unwound, his mind wandering back to the Titanic exhibit at the museum. He'd been strangely moved by it, so moved they'd spent twice as long there as they'd planned—not because of its connection to Bea but because of the reminder that after that disaster, too, just like yesterday's, Halifax had taken in the survivors. After that disaster, too, and after the explosion in 1917, thousands of people had gathered in this city, by some curious cosmic design, to breathe in the sea air while waiting to hear their fate. And lying next to Paula, now, he took some comfort in that sense of history. Took some comfort in believing that, like those thousands of others before him, this purgatory—and, soon, his others—he was going to escape. ◆

Elizabeth Cantwell

JAZZ HANDS

The sky outside is outside. We are passed
from one hand to another
like a ring taken off & fiddled with. Don't put us

down anywhere to stay. If there is a throat
it is rising. We live and die as a group, we are tethered :
cloves bound by thin, papery

skin, a war whoop
of drum sets. What comes next
or comes after. Communion : the postlude playing

us out to the hall with the tablecloths
and folding chairs, with all the little lined-up
paper plates. There's a lot of butter

in these grits : a lot of grit in these muttered
phrases, sputtering out of
horn-ends like unending, sacred prayers :

liquid air and cadence. We are the hardest to get to
the heart of. We are chili threads
left on the counter, we are pickled vegetables, filets

cut too thin. We are held by many hands now :
orison, evergreen. Tiramisu, offering. Take these ribs
and make them sing.

Sai Sai (Xi Xi)

BUTTERFLIES ARE LIGHTSOME THINGS

(translated by Jennifer Feeley)

gradually I learned
that I had turned
into a kangaroo

a kangaroo's pouch
is in its chest
mine's a pocket
in the locket of my heart

wherever I go
catching z's or wide-awake
it's chock-a-block
around the clock
with stuff I have to lug around

I'd like to dump
the whole amount
—can it all be chucked right out?
but how to forgo
and how to let go

so gradually I've come to see
why butterflies can flutter by
cuz why   cuz why
cuz butterflies are lightsome things
because   because
butterflies lack heartstrings

Hsia Yü

COOK UP WAYS TO GET HIM DEEPLY INTO SOMETHING

(translated by Steve Bradbury)

The universe is expanding, no?
But have you noticed?
In another apartment
On another couch
Another potato is lying
Who is also dying to be loved
Who can't wait for some someone to come and say:
There are things that resist intrusion
Resist the transference of affection
Resist our being on the same wavelength
He must immediately terminate the exchange
Enlarge the aesthetic distance
And then he'll feel so much better
There's no one special in my life right now
Plenty of neighbors though

My neighbor doesn't know
I've always been ashamed of the human race
Life of course is one big gala
Though some neighbors feel
Most people are just a pack of tedious partygoers
I really didn't know
My neighbor also stares at animals
He's drawing so close to the face of the cat
He has the feeling of being released
As Lévi-Strauss once put it
As far as animals go he has an instinctive understanding

Jason Freure

STILL LIFE WITH JUAN GRIS

I do not have a newspaper on my table.
I am not part of the newspaper generation.
There is one apple in my fruit bowl and many limes.

Le Devoir does not disappear under a fruit bowl
on my kitchen table. I do not scribble in *Le Devoir*'s margins.

The free weeklies pile up on my kitchen table for months.
How can I huddle at my kitchen table
when it does not sit next to a frozen window
and my floor is made of corrugated vinyl?

My kitchen table is next to an electric oven.
Grocery bags and dirty plates hoard my kitchen table.
I call it: Studio frijole.

Crumbs fill the crevices of my living room.
Broccoli rots on my kitchen table.

Cockroach, keep my dropped frijoles
but do not sneak up on my paloma jimador
when I drink at my kitchen table.

Why won't the grocer wrap my rib eye in *Le Devoir*?
Black and white and bled all over. My rib eyes can't bleed
in his Saran wrap.

Le Devoir sits on my table. Broccoli flourishes so beautifully
from my fruit bowl. A cockroach licks the ice in my paloma
jimador cocktail glass. Who ate my apple?

There is bleach on my kitchen table.
I burned the fruit bowl in the backyard.
I subscribed to *Le Devoir* dot com.

Curtis Rogers

IS TO A FIRE

We go easy on the carmine boy. Show him the egg-

shaped scrapes on our twin stomachs. Greenhouse his macho

softspot. Syrettes of the scent of hands in wine.

Yann Coridian

SEAGULLS & FIG NEWTONS

(translated by Edward Gauvin)

T arragon?"
       "Duh, dumbass, it's not *Chicken with Basil*, it's *Chicken à la Tourangelle.*"

"Look, I got three hours' sleep last night, I'm beat, and I wasn't sure for a minute. That's allowed, right? So 'dumbass' yourself—just lay off. You're my kid brother, which means you owe me respect for all time, and—"

"So...you okay with the rest? Who are you making it for, anyway? What for?"

"For us. Just us and the kids."

We hung up. He said "Love you." I didn't. I glanced out the window to see if my scooter was still down where I'd left it. There it was. I don't have a lock, so I can't help checking every now and then.

On the window ledge across the street there's a seagull, right in front of me. Watching me. I'm sure it's watching me. A seagull is a big bird. Enormous, even. I don't remember there being gulls in Paris when I was a kid. Not by the Avenue de l'Observatoire. Or, for that matter, by the Place d'Italie, where I lived after that, when my brother was born. Rue Paulin-Merry.

I'm still leaning out the window when I suddenly start jonesing for a cigarette. I used to enjoy smoking like this, by the window, when I used to smoke. Back before...I spent a lot of time at this window, doing nothing. Besides smoking, I mean—just puffing away.

There are two gulls now. A couple? There's almost no room left on the narrow ledge. The new gull's staring at me too. I can't bring myself to look away. Down below, the cars are driving around like usual, the pedestrians are doing their pedestrian thing, and nobody seems to notice a third bird is coming in to roost right by the others. Just like in "The Birds." What if that really happened? What if hundreds of them showed up all of a sudden?

I close the window and pull the curtain shut, cursing myself for being such a moron. Better get the chicken going. If I'd had a gun, I could've tried to kill one of the gulls. I probably would have hit one—not with the first shot, of course, but the third or fourth. It would've hit the sidewalk like a rock after sliding gracefully off the Thai restaurant awning, and I would've gone down, picked it up, and come back. Like nothing happened.

Seagull à la Tourangelle—Tourain style. No one would've been the wiser. Clucks of pleasure; mouth, belly, and gullet sounds: gastric symphony surrounding this roasted seagull dressed in all its tarragon.

I open the freezer and take out the chicken I got at the farm in Oucques. The organic one. Well, the Belgian one, but organic, too.

I check the time on my busted phone. Since I still haven't fixed the cracked screen, I can't see a thing. So I turn on the radio. That woman whose voice I can't stand tells me that it's 9:15 A.M.

I'm in time to defrost the chicken. I put it on a plate and then pop it all atop the percolating coffeemaker. The heat from the coffeepot will speed up defrosting. Sometimes I wish I were small enough to be put on a plate and defrosted in the morning coffee vapors. And I'd be left to melt, melt away and disappear.

-2 farm-raised organic chickens, cut into pieces
-½ bottle of excellent dry white wine
-2 teaspoons of tarragon, chopped
-4 shallots, chopped
-2 cloves of garlic, smashed
-2 cups of Cognac
-1 lemon
-3 egg yolks
-4 tablespoons butter
-30 pearl onions, sautéed in butter
-1 lb. white mushrooms, cooked in butter

It's my father's recipe. Actually, it's from an *Elle* recipe card dating back to my childhood. He made the same dish for birthday meals without fail. Served with wild rice.

He died from a ruptured aneurysm, in a car, on the highway near Clermont-Ferrand. I had to go get his things from the wreckge: a travel bag with three summer outfits, a digressive Weyergans novel (*3 Days at My Mother's*), and on the passenger seat, a smashed packet of Fig Newtons and his linen jacket, all wrinkled up. With 50 euros in his wallet, which I kept.

I robbed my dead father.

Which will probably come back to bite me in the ass someday.

Whatever. Whatever.

Also, I ate the Fig Newtons. ◆

Cynthia Cruz

ON THE TRAIN TO VERSAILLES

I.

Cracked glass of Christ
in its silver vessel, an ambulatory vitrine.

The relic of my broken
glass jar of Chanel

Vamp polish, spilled black
dreg at the bottom of my leather bag.

I'm moving, again.

II.

Of anesthesia. Of tin bins of names
piled up in numbers.

A Bela Tarr-like winter: an old water-
pocked calendar discovered among the ruins.

The blacking archive of history,
all the sweet windows finally sealed shut.

Paul Nemser

LETTER FROM BERLIN

Stones—not ruins,
but blocks again.

The buildings like headlines.

Clouds of people who read here once—
are they reading again?

Glass
breaks and gives back the street.

It is still icy here.
Black-skid taxis by the embassies,
the Tiergarten.

Chimpanzees whoop for apples
from their enclosure.

I overheard someone say
he saw the ostriches mating,
saw their hot, individual breaths.

All April first I've dreamt and redreamt
that everyone's feet are asleep,

everyone is strange
to the spring snow,

daring to trudge
through these peaceful-frantic-
shaded-by-cranes-placing-I-beams

gardens.

What can't be undone?
said the night builders,

waking me before there were birds,
the first
a nightingale.

SUBMISSION

from: **John Edwards** <johnedwards23@gmail.com>
to: Simon Cole <simoncoleed@torrentsquare.com>
date: Wed, Jan 9, 2013 at 9:05 a.m.
subject: Short Story Submission

Dear Mr. Cole,

Please consider my short story *Death of a Literary Agent* for publication in Torrent Square. I'm a huge fan of your journal, and I'm supremely impressed by how you've managed, in just a few short years, to take the literary scene by storm, putting lesser publications with bloated reputations who shall remain nameless (but are based in Portland, OR, and the San Francisco Bay Area) to shame. My fiction and essays have appeared, or are forthcoming, in New Yorke Times, Paris Reviewer, Huffington Poster, and McSwainey's. I await a response with a fool's hope.

Yours Sincerely,
John Edwards, Writer-at-Large

from: **Simon Cole** <simoncoleed@torrentsquare.com>
to: John Edwards <johnedwards23@gmail.com>
date: Tues, Jan 14, 2013 at 9:36 a.m.
subject: Short Story Submission

Dear Mr. Edwards,

Thank you for your kind words regarding our journal. To clarify: do you mean to say that you have pieces published or forthcoming in *New York Times*, *Paris Review*, Huffington Post, and *McSweeney's*?

Best Regards,
Simon Cole, Editor-in-Chief, Torrent Square

from: **John Edwards** <johnedwards23@gmail.com>
to: Simon Cole <simoncoleed@torrentsquare.com>
date: Tues, Jan 14, 2013 at 9:37 a.m.
subject: Short Story Submission

Dear Mr. Cole,
    No.
Yours Sincerely,
John Edwards, Writer-at-Large

from: **Simon Cole** <simoncoleed@torrentsquare.com>
to: John Edwards <johnedwards23@gmail.com>
date: Tues, Jan 14, 2013 at 10:14 a.m.
subject: Short Story Submission

Dear Mr. Edwards,
    Well, what do you mean, then?
Best Regards,
Simon Cole, Editor-in-Chief, Torrent Square

from: **John Edwards** <johnedwards23@gmail.com>
to: Simon Cole <simoncoleed@torrentsquare.com>
date: Tues, Jan 14, 2013 at 10:20 a.m.
subject: Short Story Submission

Dear Mr. Cole,
    New Yorke Times is a neighborhood newsletter I edit and publish that chronicles the comings, goings, and derring doings of the denizens of the City Park South neighborhood in Denver, CO; Paris Reviewer is a 'zine that I edit and publish that features the literary stylings of the denizens of the City Park South neighborhood in Denver, CO; Huffington Poster is a blog that I edit and publish that covers the political machinations in the city of Denver, specifically as they relate to the City Park South neighborhood; and McSwainey's is a literary hodge-podge, collective, what-have-you that a friend of mine founded; he lives in the City Park South neighborhood of Denver, CO.
Sincerely,
John Edwards, Writer-at-Large

from: **Simon Cole** <simoncoleed@torrentsquare.com>
to: John Edwards <johnedwards23@gmail.com>
date: Tues, Jan 14, 2013 at 11:21 a.m.
subject: Short Story Submission

Mr. Edwards,
    I'm almost at a loss for words—do you not see any potential problems from claiming publication in entities that share similar monikers to some of the highest regarded publications in the country? Entities,

I might add, whose names in no way suggest that they have anything to do with the City Park South neighborhood of Denver, CO? I suggest you re-think your approach to publication lest you be regarded a liar.
Regards,
Simon Cole, Editor-in-Chief, Torrent Square

from: **John Edwards** <johnedwards23@gmail.com>
to: Simon Cole <simoncoleed@torrentsquare.com>
date: Tues, Jan 14, 2013 at 11:24 a.m.
subject: Short Story Submission

Dear Mr. Cole,
    Well, "liar," I think, is a bit harsh. The "entities," as you call them, do, in fact, exist, and I have, in point of fact, been published in them. Any similarity, in name or otherwise, to existing or defunct periodicals is purely coincidental.
    But what did you think of my story?
Sincerely,
John Edwards, Writer-at-Large

from: **Simon Cole** <simoncoleed@torrentsquare.com>
to: John Edwards <johnedwards23@gmail.com>
date: Tues, Jan 14, 2013 at 11:36 a.m.
subject: Short Story Submission

Mr. Edwards,
    Unfortunately, your story doesn't fit our needs at this time.
Simon Cole, Editor-in-Chief, Torrent Square

from: **Kim Nguyen** <kimnguyen23@gmail.com>
to: Simon Cole <simoncole@torrentsquare.com>
date: Wed, Jan 15, 2013 at 9:05 a.m.
subject: Short Story Submission

Dear Mr. Cole,
    My name is Kim Nguyen, and I am a Burmese refugee. I'm seeking outlet for publication of excerpts of my memoir, soon to be published in its entirety, that chronicles the persecution, imprisonment, and subsequent escape from prison I experienced in the Republic of the Union of Myanmar as a disciple of the famous human rights activist Aung San Suu Kyi. I have only been in the United States for three months. When asking which publication I should seek, I was told that yours was a most respected journal, one of gravitas.

Yours Sincerely,
Ms. Kim Nguyen, Refugee

from: **Simon Cole** <simoncoleed@torrentsquare.com>
to: Kim Nguyen <kimnguyen23@gmail.com>
date: Wed, Jan 15, 2013 at 9:09 a.m.
subject: Short Story Submission

Dear Ms. Nguyen,
       Is this John Edwards?
Best Regards,
Simon Cole, Editor-in-Chief, Torrent Square

from: **Kim Nguyen** <kimnguyen23@gmail.com>
to: Simon Cole <simoncoleed@torrentsquare.com>
date: Wed, Jan 15, 2013 at 9:10 a.m.
subject: Short Story Submission

Dear Mr. Cole,
       Yes. How did you know?
Sincerely,
Ms. Kim Nguyen, Refugee

from: **Simon Cole** <simoncoleed@torrentsquare.com>
to: Kim Nguyen <kimnguyen23@gmail.com>
date: Wed, Jan 15, 2013 at 9:13 a.m.
subject: Short Story Submission

Mr. Edwards,
       Lucky guess. And "Nguyen" is a Vietnamese name. You are
beneath contempt. You will never be published in Torrent Square. And
I will reach out to every editor I know and see that they're aware of you.
Simon Cole, Editor-in-Chief, Torrent Square

from: **Kim Nguyen** <kimnguyen23@gmail.com>
to: Simon Cole <simoncole@torrentsquare.com>
date: Wed, Jan 15, 2013 at 9:15 a.m.
subject: Short Story Submission

Dear Mr. Cole,
       I hate to break it to you, Simon, but you've already published me
three times over the last eighteen months. Remember the personal
essay written by the one-legged amputee whose dream was to set the

Guinness Book of World Records record for longest pogoing session (of the punk rock dance variety, rather than with a stick)? Yeah, that was me. And remember the blind African American lady who sent you that beautiful, poignant, and harrowing short story about a fishing excursion gone awry in the Adirondacks? Me again. And who could forget the muscular, dirtily realistic short story written, some might say ironically, by a former beauty pageant winner about the hockey enforcer who was secretly afraid to fight? Not you, I'll bet—because you sure raved about it in the acceptance note. Anyway, as you can see, we're already within the walls. Sleep tight.

Sincerely,

Ms. Kim Nguyen, Refugee, and John Edwards, Writer-at-Large

from: **Simon Cole** <simoncoleed@torrentsquare.com>
to: John Edwards <johnedwards23@gmail.com>
date: Mon, Jan 20, 2013 at 9:10 a.m.
subject: Short Story Submission

Mr. Edwards,

Well, I have to admit, you had me pretty worried there for a minute. But then I contacted Ms. Marguerite Tolton via e-mail and asked if I might speak with her over the phone. She had an upstate New York telephone exchange, and, I have to tell you, after speaking with her for twenty minutes, I came away convinced that she is indeed an African American lady who was born without the benefit of sight. If that was you, continuing to pull the wool over my eyes, then you shouldn't be writing; you should be acting.

I also had occasion to visit with Mr. Henry Garfield, who, as luck would have it, resides here in the greater Boston area (as do I). He does indeed have but one leg, and while he hasn't yet achieved his dream of a Guinness World Record, he still attends many punk rock shows (some at the Middle East club in Cambridge, mere minutes from my house!), and pogos quite often, and remains confident that one day he will go for the record. Now, that wasn't you, was it? The one thing I did come away believing from your correspondence is that you truly live in the City Park South neighborhood of Denver, CO. You didn't fly to Massachusetts, have your leg amputated, and adopt a Boston brogue just to keep up your masterful deception, did you?

I was, unfortunately, unable to contact Ms. Mary Elizabeth Anania, the author of my favorite piece of the bunch, the one about the hockey goon, but I'm confident that she, too, will prove to be an actual person and not a figment of yours.

I don't understand you, Mr. Edwards. If you put half as much ener-

gy into the writing and the publishing of your stories as you do into the manufacturing of bona fides, I'm sure your stories would already be in print.
Simon Cole, Editor-in-Chief, Torrent Square

from: **John Edwards** <johnedwards23@gmail.com>
to: Simon Cole <simoncoleed@torrentsquare.com>
date: Mon, Jan 20, 2013 at 9:45 a.m.
subject: Short Story Submission

Dear Simon,

Yours was the twentieth—twentieth!—rejection of that story. And you wonder why I try and tip the odds just a smidge in my favor? *Death of a Literary Agent* is a great fucking story. But you guys are all the same (editors). What, I'm supposed to believe that you're not an insular, self-perpetuating collection of like-minded "aesthetes," more interested in your idea of how a story should operate than the actual prose in front of your face? Rare is the story that makes it into the illustrious pages of an American literary journal from the slush pile. You need an agent just to get read at the top journals in the country. And what percentage of pieces that you published last year came from authors that you—or someone on your staff, or some colleague—didn't know and recommend? Sure, there are a few pubs out there interested in discovering new talent—but the rest of you make up a nepotistic, crony-rewarding morass. You're a cabal. You're worse than Congress. To hell with you.
SINCERELY,
John Edwards, Writer-at-Large

from: **Simon Cole** <simoncoleed@torrentsquare.com>
to: John Edwards <johnedwards23@gmail.com>
date: Mon, Jan 20, 2013 at 10:50 a.m.
subject: Short Story Submission

Dear Mr. Edwards,

Surely we're not as bad as Congress?

You know, I just read the story you submitted, and you're right: it is quite good. You are a good writer. But it didn't strike me the way a story needs to for me to publish it. Which doesn't mean it won't strike another editor. I sympathize with you, John, I really do. I'm not just an editor; I'm a writer, too. And I'm no stranger to a rejection notice. Do you know how many stories and essays I read each year? Hundreds. Hundreds! And out of those hundreds, I have to pick a select few that affect me in such a way that I think, "Jesus Christ, I've been moved; it doesn't seem possible as long as I've been at this, but I've been moved. Again. I have to put this before people; I have to champion this." It's not personal. The rejection. I mean it. It's not. These are judgment calls that I make, and I don't make them lightly. Do I publish stories by people I know? Yes. Do I pay more attention to one piece because of a person who advocates for it, whether it's a colleague or an agent? Yes. But no piece I publish isn't held to a high standard that's consistent regardless of who the author is. Believe me, I've pissed off some big-name writers by rejecting material that I didn't think was worthy of publication in Torrent Square. And I'd solicited some of those writers! Insult to injury!

It's definitely tough to break into literary publishing for a little-known author. But I'm going to give you some advice that I was once given, that I've followed, and that I believe is the reason I stuck it out in literary publishing, both as a writer and an editor: it's a war of attrition, so here's how you fight that war: always have ten pieces out at all times; when one of those pieces gets rejected, immediately send it to another journal; when one of them gets published, send another piece into the fray. You've got to be Ulysses S. Grant. Keep pouring in the troops until you overwhelm your enemy.

Good luck. I really do wish you the best in your writing. I hope you persevere. You've got talent. Don't sully it with dishonesty.
Best Regards (truly),
Simon Cole, Editor-in-Chief, Torrent Square

from: **John Edwards** <johnedwards23@gmail.com>
to: Simon Cole <simoncoleed@torrentsquare.com>
date: Mon, Jan 20, 2013 at 11:05 a.m.
subject: Short Story Submission

Simon,

I know, ostensibly, that the rejections aren't personal, but do you know how long I've worked on some of these damn stories? Years, for some of them. Fucking years. I started *Literary Agent* in 2009. The one I sent you is the sixteenth draft. How can I not take it personally when you reject it? It *is* personal. It couldn't be more personal. I'm sorry I lied to you. What can I say? I'm desperate.

from: **Simon Cole** <simoncoleed@torrentsquare.com>
to: John Edwards <johnedwards23@gmail.com>
date: Mon, Jan 20, 2013 at 11:15 a.m.
subject: Short Story Submission

John,

I'll tell you what: send me another story, and let's see if it hits that chord.

Simon Cole, Editor-in-Chief, Torrent Square

from: **John Edwards** <johnedwards23@gmail.com>
to: Simon Cole <simoncoleed@torrentsquare.com>
date: Mon, Jan 20, 2013 at 11:16 a.m.
subject: Short Story Submission

Dear Simon,

I already did. I uploaded it to your site three days ago. It's under the name "Mildred Martin." Sorry about that. Last time—I swear!

Sincerely,

John Edwards, Writer-at-Large

P.S. Also, you probably don't want to waste any more time trying to contact Ms. Mary Elizabeth Anania, the author of the hockey enforcer story. If you Google that appellation along with "maiden name" you'll see why. And then you'll know that my name isn't really John Edwards. It's actually Abe Brennan. Nice to really meet you. And again: sorry.

P.P.S. But let me know what you think of my story!

.

Lucy Biederman

ELEGY ON THE OCCASION OF THE U.S. GLOBAL CHANGE RESEARCH PROGRAM'S THIRD NATIONAL CLIMATE CHANGE ASSESSMENT, MAY 2014

to the ends of the
president & back
is there time to undress
the nation before
the monuments I desire

in Washington
seeking a feeling
my therapist waiting
in a shield of a
building in Dupont

her little haircuts
outfits & maternity leave
was how I became me
it's too late okay
but I touched the anchor

—*written on*
the rising sea

WRITER'S PROCESS

What do I know? I try to make a joke of it when I teach or go to some-one's classroom to talk about my poetry. I just say, I don't really know anything, you have your own life and world that's as full and real and true, probably more so. Everyone is just one person, no one is two people.

I see old poets, or poets my age, or cute young poets, professing on the Internet. I want to stick a pin in their authority and be the only one. I want to slice through the world like a Nietzsche aphorism. I used to be a cute young poet, and someday hopefully I'll be an old poet; what did I know, what will I know? Who wants advice, wisdom, letters? I have my weird choices to keep me company, my own way of doing things, a mosaic of mistakes.

Literary theory is one of my favorite things because it feels endless, and it shows how literature touches every part of living. I didn't know there were formulations for things like *ontology* before I started learning about literary theory. I need such huge concepts to think about climate change, because if the world is going to end, or if we might approach that end the way we did during the Cuban Missile Crisis (I heard someone say on the radio, "You have no idea how close we came"), I need to try to prepare a neat pack, like packing a suitcase, out of the way I have moved through the made world.

When I wrote "Elegy" I felt a sense of doom that feels a little bit humorous now, because lately I've scarcely given a thought to climate change leading to the end of life as we know it. Lately I have been think-ing—assuming, actually—that humankind will come up with some eleventh-hour fix for this wretched environmental situation, some moon colony as yet unimagined. They say one of the greatest hurdles to wide-spread social action toward environmental sustainability is peoples' inability to conceive of such an enormous problem facing humanity. To try to recover the doom, I looked at my journal from around when I was working on the poem:

> I know there must be another way of seeing it, but the more I think of global warming the more I think of how much of life it will and does encompass, everything we use and are. There's noth-ing more important. The Emerson readings we've been doing for the class I teach—if you can find yourself in Nature—that it would be this unchanging, repeating thing— What self do you find in Nature when the Nature that reflects the self back at you is utterly altered by the way we ruined the environment?
>
> And it will never be the same again. We could all die because of this. Everyone, our entirely legacy of humanity—it could all be over.
>
> Maybe, in the galaxy, *that* I lived, that we all did, might mean something. The terrible things we did and said and the weapons we

aimed at each other could leave some trace. But maybe not.

They always talk about how time is a construct, but when a certain time is over, there is a way that it's really over. At least, you cannot access something that is over in the same way you can access the present or future. You can't live within it or toward it with the same sense of collective feeling.

Living together on earth: I feel like I'm already starting to miss it. It makes me feel so miserable to consider it all being over. I remember the Gap on Halsted Street we always used to go to when it was time to get new clothes, I was always so excited. It's not there anymore, and it hasn't been there for a long long time. I remember the little mini arcade on Main Street in Ann Arbor with secret shops inside it. I always picture it when I think of Walter Benjamin. I wondered who shopped at those stores. It was like there was a whole secret community living in the town of people who weren't in my program. I remember feeling like I could picture my whole life taking place there, but that didn't happen at all. So what was that? What was I picturing? It was just a dream, and now I only remember the dream, not what it felt like to feel it. That time is so over. I cannot touch it. And soon the world that ever held it won't be touchable.

Now I remember the doom.

There are a bunch of scenes I think of often: being only four and sitting in the sun in my dad's lap on this brown chair we used to have; or walking by this fence in the evening near the house I lived in with an ex-boyfriend. When I think of them, it seems like that one single event, that scene, is all I have, and all I have ever thought or moved away from. Sort of like Derrida's center that limits free play: an organizing, comforting thing that holds you away from the hell-chaos of real life, *and* a weird hell-chaos thing itself, in how it holds you away. The most famous example of this in poetry is Wallace Stevens's "Anecdote of the Jar": setting a jar in a hill organizes the "slovenly wilderness," everything is suddenly either jar or not-jar. That jar makes the wilderness "no longer wild." Just a *jar* to separate us from utter wildness, chaos, the chasm of meaningless over and over forever, structurelessness that never stops repeating. I hold on *hard* to who I say I am, just an *am*, a random epistemological construction that could roll down the hill and disappear from sight during a hard rain.

Erin was my therapist when I lived in Northern Virginia, and I saw her for six years, on and off. When I remember specific scenes from my times with her, I see the organizing centers I came to *choose*. I still need tons of help living: pills, time off, unearned money, special treatment. But Erin helped me find some ways of coping that I bump into all the time inside myself, daily, and those things are not a joke, not something I don't know; they're who I am and how I make it through. So if it's going to be the end, I'll say that that's my story. —L.B.

J. Camp Brown

EARTHEN HOUSE

Mortar perish. Weather
batter and burrow
it, but mud

moss, clover trowel
any cranny twixt
bricks

until to dig out would
cause collapse
though

collapse do loom:—whether
rained rotten or
felled

by a felled tree:—its seed
need only a crawl
space of light

to root and bloom, a window
to grow toward
to shatter.

Yao Feng

UNTITLED

(translated by Tam Hio Man and Kit Kelen)

the potato hibernating in the cellar
sprouts poison fingers
to conduct the music of spring's combo

a strain of grey hair dyed black
makes a white elephant stumble

we've used death
to invent a verb

an ox sent to the slaughter house
is ruminating tears

Sandra Simonds

BREAD (AFTER PONGE)

Holy shit the surface of bread is fucking amazing and gives off
the same phantasmagoric light that it takes—a diorama of light
from the Alps, the Andes, the Sierras—where amorphous figures
from pages of history books surface—where a mass of trains and
airplanes glisten under some stellar factories and then someone
throws a few thousand falcons and trees into the pot...and voilà!

This bread is a noble sight!—made from the skin of the cow,
visions of Siamese twins, hangnails, ancient hanging gardens,
mussels pulled from the seashore and, of course, a little bit of the
flowering sky, the steamy aprons and exhalations of all the men
and women and little babies you love.

If you open your mouth for one second, Felix, when the clock
strikes midnight tonight and tiptoe into your little checkered
kitchen, and eat one tiny crumb, you will know exactly what I am
talking about.

Christopher Patton

(C)LEAR

I was at a centre of things.
Wrens at life in holes around me in woodrot.
Little, being,
the king's amiss,
his sky a bough
of mouths.

Death of the royal principle (ego).
The nearer they came to look
at him, the closer he was
to gone to them.

The earth they walk on's an own-study.
Earth I'm under, another no
one owns. Sing
that, asshole.

Because we die?
We always all died.

Little little.
Spike of sunblack
at the temple.
           All's well
in hell, an they eat from
each others' mouths.

Lynn Gordon

TELEKINESIS

The first time I saw my husband, he had a red satin cape, and magnificent dark hair in a ponytail down his back. He swallowed razor blades and spat them back out again. He breathed a huge aura of fire. He stapled a five-dollar bill to his forehead and pounded nails into his nose, taking them out afterward with pliers.

All this made me feel hopelessly run-of-the-mill, so that when he began chatting with me after the performance, I told him I could bend spoons with my brain waves, like Uri Geller—telekinesis. Right away he wanted to see me do it. I picked a spoon off a caterer's cart and held it up. I rubbed it and rubbed it, just at the tip of the handle, and he watched me in the most flattering way. I was prepared to work that spoon for an hour, just to keep his attention.

As it happened, something came up before long to make him glance to the side: a woman scolding someone who had jostled her coffee cup. The instant James glanced away, I seized the spoon in both hands and bent it with all my might. By the time his eyes flicked back to me, I had the spoon back in position, holding it the same as before, only now the bowl was curved over like a swan's head on its neck.

He said it was impressive, really great, and I could see he meant it. I supposed that was why he invited me to eat a picnic with him the following weekend. He drove me out to the coast and we sat on the sand, eating from a foam cooler he'd brought along. There were carrots and red peppers to dip into curried mayonnaise, boiled eggs, and sandwiches with turkey and smoked gouda. Because it was July, the wind blew fiercely. We huddled into a recessed area along the cliffs, but still particles of sand ground between my teeth and no doubt between his, too. I scarcely noticed them when we began kissing.

Despite his intimidating abilities, James was tremendously nice, and he never forgot what I had done with the spoon. He mentioned it when he asked to marry me. "I can't let someone like you slip through my fingers," he said. "I've never in my life met a woman, or a man either, who could bend a spoon through mental concentration. You're a wonder, and anyway we get along perfectly." It always seemed funny to me that he was fooled, being a magician himself and well schooled in the art of misdirection.

We married, of course, and settled in Redwood City, in a cottage with bougainvillea at the door. I was twenty-eight and James a little younger. He traveled around the area, especially on weekends, to perform in San Francisco and all sorts of places. I kept on with my hairdressing work, dropping down to part time.

It wasn't long before I came to learn more about James's act. Some things were tricks and some were real. The five-dollar bill on the forehead, for example, that was a trick involving adhesive; he didn't actually have a staple piercing his skin. But the nails up the nose were real. They can go safely through the nostrils and into the nasal cavity; you just have to practice and be careful. In fact, James eventually caused a bit of damage—a nail went awry—and the result was a sniffle that never got entirely better.

James did a great deal of practicing; he wanted to be first-rate. He worked on a good many different bits, some that he found in leaflets and some of his own invention: pulling a dozen eggs out of his mouth, one after another; making beer freeze solid in three seconds. He even developed a sort of striptease, in which he hooked a coat hanger through a chain at his neck. He'd take off his jacket and put it on the hanger, and then remove all his other clothing from behind the jacket, hanging each item as he went along. At the end, he turned around and you could see the black ponytail and his bare back and buttocks, proving that all was as it seemed. The act was a beauty once he'd learned it well, and I loved seeing him that way, at the end, the muscled line from his shoulders to his feet forming an almost perfect V.

In the early days, I sometimes traveled with James to a party or a club where they'd hired him for the evening. I'd sit off in a corner and hug myself, watching him. I used to hope that his eyes would find me in the audience, and that he'd do something—with everyone watching—that was meant specially for me, although I knew that such behavior was unprofessional; he had to maintain his focus.

I thought of James lots of times while I cut hair. Of course I would never take a scissors to his; he wouldn't have let me touch it in any case. I mostly did washes and cuts for old ladies at a large rest home called Bonita Terrace. I kept regular hours there on Wednesdays and Saturdays, with plenty of clients because so many of the ladies liked to have weekly appointments. One of them, Mrs. Stewart, even told me forthrightly that what mattered was that I touched them—rubbed their scalps and pinned locks of hair—and it was nearly all the touching they got anymore, except when they visited the doctor. They were starved for that sort of contact, which is what made me think of James, his touching my cheeks and running a knuckle over my lips; all of that

that he did. At the end of my work day, I would bicycle home propelled by gratitude.

James didn't consort much with other magicians, but one late-summer day he phoned me at home and said he was bringing a friend—"very clever, you'll like him"—to have dinner with us. I immediately began to devise a new menu, feeling we should have something better than the hamburgers I'd planned. I tinkered awhile, ran out for ingredients, and, half an hour before James was due home, slid a spanakopita into the oven under a sheet of foil. Then I scrubbed myself in the shower and changed into slacks and a blouse with a lace insert below the collar.

I stood cutting tomatoes and olives when James came in the front door. His entrance was always a marvel to me—that he, being who he was, was coming home to me, of all people. He stepped close and kissed me, and just after that the door opened again and a man came in. He had a lean face with pockmarks in the hollows of his cheeks, combed-back hair with grease in it. He stood at a little distance and James reached an arm toward him, saying, "This is Florian. Florian, my wife, Shell."

"A pleasure," he said. He didn't try to shake hands, I suppose because I still held the knife sunk halfway through a tomato. He hung back, but not in an awkward way at all. It wasn't until we sat down to eat that he spoke to me again. He said the spanakopita was delicious: "Not my usual fare."

James laughed at that. "Florian's a sword swallower," he explained. "One of just a few in the world." He looked quite proud to know such a person.

My heart twitched. "Is it real?" Florian cocked his head slightly. "I mean, is it a trick, like James with his razor blades?"

Florian set his face straight toward me then. I could see pale fragments of the dinner between his teeth; spanakopita is a messy dish that way. "It's absolutely real," he said. "You'll have to come see it. Maybe James and I will be performing together one of these days."

"He risks his life," James said. "All of them; they practice for years, but there's no getting around it." I thought of a sharp, heavy blade down inside me, running through my throat to my stomach, and it made me shudder. "It's mind over matter." James patted his napkin against his mouth. Suddenly he lit up, so that I was afraid of what he would say next. "Like you, Shell."

I tried to change the subject by offering more salad, but James was turning to Florian in excitement, claiming his attention. "You should see what Shell can do. The only person I've met who can perform telekinesis. First time I met her, she bent a spoon for me, just doubled it over, and I knew she was the one."

"Is that so?" said Florian. His grey eyes glinted as if he had needles in them. Unexpectedly, he winked at me. "Perhaps, if I am a very good guest, you might demonstrate for me."

I was fiercely chewing my salad, and washing it down with gulps of red wine.

"Even I have only witnessed it once," said James, and I could see he was longing to impress Florian. "It was so spectacular, I'm not sure I want her to repeat it. I prefer just to remember the occasion. I watched her holding the spoon, and suddenly it drooped over . . . so far, all at once. It was amazing."

"That would certainly be something to see," said Florian. He speared up a slice of tomato, and that occupied him for a moment. I saw that I had dripped wine onto our tablecloth; the pinkish spots were blurring at the edges as the stain was drawn into the fabric.

Florian smiled, again showing residues of food between his straight, pointed teeth. "I have a solution that should suit all of us. What if Shell does it for me alone? You don't have to watch, James."

"Oh, I don't know." I stood up quite suddenly. "I'm just going to get a sponge for these spots."

"There we go! Wouldn't you like to, Shell?" said James, overlapping my own words. "While you're in the kitchen, bring back a spoon."

I pretended not to hear. I came back with the sponge and began to dab at the tablecloth. I squeezed water over the spots and then rubbed hard, so that bits of the sponge started to crumble off. Meanwhile, James stood up and fetched a spoon himself. He put his arm over my shoulders and took the sponge from me. "You take Florian in the living room and show him how it's done. I'll hide away in the bedroom for a few minutes." He beamed and handed me the spoon.

So it happened that Florian poised himself on a footstool in our living room while I stood alone before him. He gazed up at me and winked for a second time. "Go ahead," he said. "I can hardly wait."

"Well, it doesn't always work. I'm out of practice."

He continued to stare at me. The cheese-laden, fatty smell of the spanakopita lingered in the air, and I had to fight the urge to open a window. I held up the spoon as I had with James and began to rub the handle, watching Florian carefully to catch him in a moment of distraction. I hoped that a car would go by, or that James would make a noise from the bedroom, or that Florian's mind would wander of its own accord. For uncountable minutes we were locked in our tableau of telekinesis, during which nothing moved except my fingers. I wanted to be away somewhere, snipping blue-grey curls and fluffing them, shaving the nape of a neck and seeing the skin shiver under my razor.

My hand was aching as I worked the thin steel handle, wondering if I would ever have an opportunity for my deception, when I noticed that Florian's gaze seemed to have dropped to the lace insert of my blouse, or possibly below.

It was my only chance, I felt. I needed to grab the opportunity and then the torment would be over. I glanced toward the window, hoping that Florian might also glance in that direction, and at the same time I jammed the spoon and felt it yield under my hand. When I looked back to Florian, his eyes glinted more than ever.

"Aha. I hope that wasn't your best cutlery." His lips pulled wider, the barest of smiles.

"Yes." I dropped into a bow, one hand behind my back and one in front, still clutching the spoon. Something in Florian's manner confounded me.

"James!" I called, "we're done," and he came to the doorway. He looked eagerly at Florian, sniffing a little—he had already developed the sniffle by then.

Now Florian smiled fully. "It was astonishing! I've never in my life seen anything like it. You have quite a wife." James looked delighted.

They stayed in the living room to talk and drink more wine while I excused myself to the kitchen—the quiet kitchen, where only the spouting faucet made a noise. A squirt of soap went in, suds billowed up, and I plunged my hands through to the hot water. For a moment I could only lean against the sink and rest myself.

Eventually I filled the dish drainer. The sink was emptying with a throaty, drinking-straw sound when Florian walked in, presumably on his way to the john.

"You really have something with that act," he said. Then he plucked away my dish towel and pressed a card into my hand, bending his head close so that I had a near view of the comb-furrows in his oiled hair. He looked back once, with a smile, as he continued through the kitchen and out the far doorway.

I held up the card and read it slowly, the silvery writing on black cardstock that said:

Florian
of the Swords.

Below, in smaller letters, it said "Special Engagements" and gave a telephone number, with shining silver blades embossed to either side.

At a party two days later, a posh fundraiser in Atherton, everyone sat on folding chairs on a broad lawn, with a platform at the front where James was performing. Sunlight flowed between the branches of oak trees that grew to one side. James did the razor blades, which he magically linked together with a cord he swallowed, so that they came up in a series like a string of Christmas lights. I wished that, as he pulled on the cord, during the suspenseful part before any razors appeared, his glance would turn to me—that he would draw the razor blades from his mouth as an offering to me. This did not happen, of course.

When James finished his act, I clapped like mad. Everyone did. Then I pressed the back of my hand to my forehead; the heat and the excitement had caused me to perspire. I thought I was being discreet. I only touched my hand up there for a moment; I didn't swipe it across.

A man next to me tapped my arm then. He leaned toward me and held out a folded handkerchief. I had scarcely ever seen such a thing, a handkerchief. Even my father never carried one, but I guessed that rich people did—and this man had to be immensely rich to be attending the fundraiser. I took the handkerchief from him, linen with a grain you could feel, and touched it very lightly to my face, keeping it folded, as if that would save him having to wash it afterward. He was handsome, too. He had small wrinkles next to his eyes, like smiles, and an attentive way of looking at me. I thanked him, handed back his linen handkerchief, and never said another word to him. That shows how uninterested I was in anyone except James.

A week passed. On a quiet afternoon I sat in a chair by the open window, looking at cookie recipes. I'd gotten a notion to take something sweet to the ladies at Bonita Terrace. When the phone rang, I reached over and picked it up, still deep in the realm of shortbread and dream bars.

Then came the voice: "Shell, is it you?"

"Oh," I said, dazed at first. "James isn't here."

"That is perfectly all right." He drew the words out. "I have been thinking about your trick with the spoon, such a pleasure to watch."

"You liked it?" I was losing my place in the cookbook.

"I was quite fascinated, let's say. Your husband is so, so proud about it." A pause. "He is a great believer in you, I gather."

A small sound leapt out of my throat.

"Perhaps I should discuss it with him, my perceptions...and so forth."

Without thinking I said, "Don't. Please don't."

"No?" The syllable flamed up like a lighted candle. "Then suppose I discuss it with *you*. Will you come to see me?"

"Stop it." I welled up from the chair, prepared to bang the phone onto its cradle. The cookbook fell from my lap.

"You want me to leave you alone?" That was enough to keep me on the line. "I can do that," he went on, "but of course James and I cross paths. Of course I'll be talking to him. You see?"

A breeze blew in the window so that the curtains churned around my head. I batted at them.

"Shell, are you there still? You have an easy way out of this."

"When? Where?" I asked, when the breeze died down.

"That is more like it. Be sure to wear the blouse you had on at dinner."

The first time he clamped himself around me, I was fool enough to think it would only be the once. He would have his way, and in exchange he'd promised to say nothing to James. James would never know; that got me through all of it. We would be safe.

Instead I came to know his plaid couch, the spongy wall-to-wall carpet in the hallway, even his tiled kitchen counter, which left sharp little crumbs on the backs of my thighs. To the leverage he held over me to begin with, he'd added the threat of telling James about what he called my disloyalty. I should have thought of that before I got started, but I didn't.

It got to be September and we were on his bedspread. He hung just above me, and to avoid his face I looked up to the light fixture on the ceiling—a square of glass etched with a wheat-ear pattern. "You have to come more often," he said. "Every week from now on."

"I can't manage it." I had to switch to looking into his grey eyes. "I have my work, and James expects me to go along on some of his gigs." He dropped onto his back then, pulling me on top. He took a length of my hair in each hand and directed me to all the places that wanted attention.

Later we rolled back the other way and I faced the light fixture again. There was a grey smudginess behind the glass that must have been the corpses of insects.

Mrs. Stewart liked me to roll her hair in pin curls. "None of that chicken wire stuff for me. It pulls my old scalp." She told me that at the first appointment, and I said not to worry, I had plenty of bobby pins.

Now I was unclipping the curls; they hung from her head like springs. "This is a good length for you," I said. "Wait till you see it combed out."

"How's that husband, the one with the magic wand?"

"He's just fine, busy. Word's getting around."

"Ah, I can tell everything by your voice." She raised her arm to touch me with her creased fingers. "I had that with my first husband, Bernard, the loveliest man you can imagine."

She was quiet while I waved the hair dryer over her. It's that stage, with the hair barely wet, that allows the best opportunity for shaping. I combed through the curls and twisted them around my fingers for a graceful effect. None of that old-lady look of cotton batting with wisps pulled loose.

Mrs. Stewart gazed at herself in the mirror and stuck out her chin in approval. "He used to help spiders out of the house," she said, as though there had been no interruption. "Once he rescued a bird that flew in—it was knocking its head against a window, trying to escape— by throwing a towel over it. He carried it outside, to the middle of the garden, and unwrapped the towel. You should have seen! That bird flew up to a branch and sang six different songs." She pulled her head to the side, away from my hands. "Ooch, careful around the ears. I had to ignore some of his habits—running behind schedule all the time, forgetting my birthday. That kind of marriage, you do anything to make it last."

I plunged my hands into the curls and mixed them up like a salad, more for Mrs. Stewart's pleasure than for any reason of styling. "You're right," I murmured, watching her face in the mirror. Then I did the final comb-out.

It was difficult, getting away to Florian's apartment each week, but I was managing. He had begun to tie my ankles sometimes, even to tear my clothes. Once he slathered me in oil, which I could feel in my elbows and between my toes even after two hot showers and the passage of days. I asked him one time, as he was busy with my feet, about James. "He admires you so much, don't you care about him?"

Florian looked up, across the knolls of my belly and slumping breasts. "I do like him. Only I like you more; you are quite captivating." He moved forward, his face serious, and ran his thumb along my neck. When I said nothing more, he went back to my feet, doing things that kept me from thinking.

Sometimes, after visiting Florian, I drove out to the ocean and threw rocks into the water. I waded in, my hands full of stones, and heaved them while the chilling water sucked at my legs. Once I found a beer bottle on the sand and took it by the neck. I raised it high and smashed it on a rock. Then I jumped back and stared at the green shards. They had scattered over the sand, ready to cut the flesh of bare-footed lovers, children, and frolicking dogs. I knelt and picked up some of the bigger pieces, but what I had done could not be undone.

James didn't seem to notice anything, except that once, kissing me, he said I smelled different. He never mentioned Florian and I didn't either.

Winter came, and the bougainvillea at our door froze to the ground. It stayed cold and grim until the start of March—I've found that, contrary to the saying, March in San Mateo County trots in like a lamb and out like a lion. The plum trees on our street opened into blossom.

The improved weather sent us to the coast for one of our picnics, and afterward we walked through the marsh, pointing out hawks in the sky above us. Toward the end of the path, on a small rise, we found a bench and sat down. James held my hand between his thumb and finger, and said he had a surprise.

"Florian gave me tickets so that we could see him perform, next Thursday in the city."

"What?"

"The sword man? I run into him every so often. He came to dinner at our place—of course you remember him."

"I do, now that you say it." I pretended to be searching out birds and animals in the grasses below us. I had asked Florian to show me his routine, months earlier, and been refused: "I don't do swords for you, and in return I don't ask you to cut my hair." Had James persuaded him to give us the passes, or was this Florian's backhanded way of showing me what he could do?

"You did telekinesis for him. He was so impressed—still talks about it." He pulled my elbow and grinned. "Anyway, it's the chance of a lifetime; he's very daring."

"Yes, I remember him."

The event was a nurses' convention, one of those hotel ballroom places with hugely patterned carpeting and no windows. I doubted that ball gowns and fox trots had ever been seen there. Of course we hadn't paid the convention fee, hundreds of dollars; Florian had arranged special passes for James and me.

The nurses, mostly dyed-blonde women with smokers' wrinkles around their mouths, had been attending sessions on professional topics—bed sores, I imagined; kidney failure; assisting with open-heart surgery. Now they were in a party mood. They were laughing and drinking cocktails and nudging each other; at first the big-bellied announcer at the front couldn't get them to listen. We had seats in the fourth row, close enough for me to catch the man's eye and shrug in sympathy.

Finally the announcer stuck his ring fingers into his mouth and blasted a screech into the microphone. I wondered what he was doing at a nurses' meeting; he should have been a barker over in North Beach, shanghaiing tourists into the topless clubs. "Ladies and gentlemen," he cried, "to kick off our entertainment this evening, we have a rare and remarkable act to show you, one that is nevertheless of medical interest!" Some of the nurses groaned at that, and slurped from their glasses. "This is an act the likes of which you've never seen before and may never see again. Tonight we are being visited by Florian, a sword swallower of the first rank! Yes, you heard me, a truly remarkable prac- titioner of an elite and ancient art. Now I present for you... Florian of the Swords!"

"The Saber Dance" began to play; I recognized it from ice events at the Olympics. The woman sitting in front of me turned to her neighbor and shrugged, then lifted her drink in a hand that flashed with jew- elry. In a twinkling Florian bounded to his place before us, dressed all over in gold-green sequins, his hair gleaming under a spotlight. Most of the audience set down their drinks to applaud. James took my hand and held it in his lap while Florian crisscrossed the floor, flourishing a sword and swooshing the air like a baton twirler.

When the music faded, Florian came to a stop at the microphone and started a patter: the history of sword swallowing and the years of training required, with jokes thrown in. "You can only spend so much time actually doing it, so you have to build up to it," James whispered. I didn't listen very hard to Florian; his sequins were blazing into my eyes so that my head ached. I pressed my free hand to my temple.

Soon the people around us were laughing and squirming in their seats. When Florian judged them ready, he held up his sword; "The Saber Dance" came on again. Florian threw back his head, pointed the tip of the blade toward his mouth, and let it slide downward inch by inch. Then he made a deep bow, letting us see that the sword had truly gone into his mouth, that it wasn't a trick. In a moment he straightened up and drew the sword back out. James was keenly interested. "He has to be quick," he said in my ear. "You can only suppress the gag reflex for so long." The room was applauding hugely.

There ensued swallowings of longer and longer swords: sixteen inches, eighteen inches, twenty, and twenty-two. At one point Florian called a woman from the audience to stand alongside and pull the sword back out of him, then laughed when she nearly swooned. James was shaking his head with his lips tight together.

The music vanished again. "Now," Florian said, and he made himself taller under the spotlight. "You are all familiar with human anatomy, are you not? You know that the esophagus is a direct passage from throat to stomach. Is that right?" He looked around the mur- muring audience—the woman in front of me was bobbing her head vigorously—and at that moment his eyes found me.

"I have something different for you now," he said, shifting his gaze and pulling forward yet another sword from a table behind him. "Ah, but look at this." He turned the blade ninety degrees, and its bowed shape was revealed. "How, you may ask, can I send this curved saber down a straight pathway? It requires masterful skill and control, nothing more." He smiled, the hollows of his cheeks in shadow under the light.

James pinched my arm, looking stern and excited. "This is the most difficult."

"But first, I need another volunteer," said Florian. He beckoned to someone at the end of the first row. A small woman with a shag cut bounced up to join him, and Florian asked her to inspect the saber. "Is it solid, would you say? No seams, nothing collapsible about it?" The woman ran her tiny fingers over the blade and pronounced it "completely real."

"Very good," said Florian, and put something into her hands. "I have given this helpful lady a stalk of celery," he announced. "She will hold it, and now we'll take the measure of this weapon." With that, he went into a samurai posture and hacked at the celery over and over. The nurses were quiet as thin green slices fell to the floor.

The small woman returned to her seat. Florian took up a cloth and ran it over the saber's blade. That was when the smell came to me, although I don't know how it could have, in a room already lush with the scents of gin and brassy colognes. It was the smell of the oil he had rubbed me with, that had clung to my skin for days. Then Florian did what I'd always wished for from James: he put his needle gaze on me and held it there for an intent fraction of time.

This time Florian bowed his head forward to insert the saber, and my attention froze onto that blade. It was going to pass next to Florian's heart and between his lungs. As he tipped sideways to allow for the curvature, I concentrated on the blade that would move through Florian's soft, pale tissues, the vulnerable parts of him that I had never been able to touch. The tension in my head was causing me moments of blackness. Florian tipped far to the side, and the saber glided in until the hilt touched his lips. Applause boomed and rolled through the ballroom and swelled against my ears.

Florian's face lost color as he drew out the saber. Next to me, James took a sharp breath. Florian was dropping slowly, his gold-green body shimmying down until it lay on the floor. The sequins boiled under the light. For a moment there was a question of whether it was part of the performance, meant to make us laugh. Then, in the hot confusion, I heard the nurses rising around me. I stayed rigid and never stopped concentrating.

I sat at our dining table, the very one where Florian had eaten with us. I had my checkbook and a stack of bills to occupy me, but my thoughts dwelt on Florian. He had sat in the chair across from me, smiling and complimenting, his teeth bearing the traces of what we had fed him.

I ran an envelope across my tongue, tamped it shut with a fist. When James came in, he found me holding a pen over the open checkbook, not writing.

"Come tell me the news," I said.

"In a minute." I heard him opening a cupboard in the kitchen, opening the refrigerator and shutting it. Opening it again. I forced myself to make marks with the pen. At last he walked in, holding a glass of milk, and took the chair next to me.

"It's not good." His voice dropped. "There's a perforation that can't be fixed it. He won't make it."

"Definitely?" I gave up holding the pen. I could have cried out, in a high, austere way that resembled song. I kept my head down.

"Shell." He hugged me from the side, so that our ears touched.

After a moment I shifted away a little. I pulled at a bit of dead skin next to my fingernail, and blood came up. I put my thumb over it. "Did you talk to him? Did he say anything?"

"I did, but I don't think he heard me." James dipped his head to see into my face. "It's a hazard of the trade."

"But he didn't say anything?" I was getting blood on the checkbook and not even trying to wipe it up.

James shook his head. "He was an expert."

Light flowed through my arms and made the blood come out faster. I pressed hard with my thumb.

He picked up my hand and held it. "He always remarked on that telekinesis trick of yours." He shook his head again.

For a moment I couldn't move. I knew the blood was smearing between our fingers, but I held on. It was the closest I'd ever come to feeling a blade pass next to my own heart, oiled and cold. ◆

Jenna Le

COCONUT PANDAN TAPIOCA CAKE

Banh xu xe is a traditional cake that is normally served at
Vietnamese weddings. The stickiness of the cake symbolizes
the stickiness of the marriage ties. The golden filling embodies
the loyalty & faithfulness of husband & wife, like a golden heart.
—danangcuisine.com

Pandanus amaryllifolius'
svelte leaves, massed like so many shadow puppets,
mob the hut where the newlyweds make love.

The plants that swarm the portholes have a scrubbed
smell, like a grove no dog's yet grimed with droppings.
Pandanus amaryllifolius—

green fans whose roots, like water spiders, pussyfoot
in plain sight—send cockroaches galloping
from the hut where the newlyweds make love.

Like eunuchs wielding chlorophyll katanas,
the plants stand guard while the twined pair lies sleeping.
Pandanus amaryllifolius:

when morning comes, the bride will stand, hair mussed,
in her new kitchen, floury fingers plumping
sweet cakes that symbolize sweet bonded love.

No pastries she makes henceforth on that stove
will taste good as those cakes, those first flawed couplings
when *pandanus amaryllifolius*
blessed the hut where the newlyweds made love.

Thierry Horguelin

POSITIONS IN SPACE

(translated by Edward Gauvin)

You were late to the airport, and A dropped you at the curb before heading off to park the car. As you stepped through the sliding doors, the first thing your eyes sought out was the arrivals board. You were looking for B's plane, and noticed that it, too, had landed somewhat late, which makes up for your own lateness. You're relieved: you hate being late. The whole way to the airport, the thought that B might already be trying to spot you in the crowd awaiting travelers, and wondering why you weren't there, gave rise to an anxiety you knew well—an anxiety heightened by the troublesome traffic, slowed to a crawl by snowfall during the night. For a moment, you thought you'd never make it. And yet, at this very moment, B must be waiting in line at the passport check, unless he's already waiting for his luggage before the carousel. Relax—everything's fine. But as your nervous tension lets go all at once, you suddenly realize you are very tired.

According to the airport's digital clock, it is 6:46 A.M. If you and A are late, snow isn't the only reason: neither of you heard the alarm clock go off. Or rather, to be more precise, A heard it go off and reached out instinctively to hit snooze, then went right back to sleep. True, neither he nor you are used to waking up so early. Only forty minutes later, alerted by some mysterious sixth sense, did you wake up with a start. You let out a brief yell when you saw what time it was, and shook A until his teeth rattled. The two of you hightailed it out the door like a pair of maniacs, not even stopping for a bite of breakfast. Which explains why you really want a coffee right now, maybe even a chocolate croissant.

You often come to greet friends at this airport. There is, you recall, a coffee shop way down at the other end of the arrivals terminal, where you could grab a double espresso to go. The thing is, what would happen if you left right now? Probably A would pick this exact moment to turn up from the parking structure, or B would emerge from the baggage claim. These two things could also both happen at the same time: A and B would run into each other and wonder where you've gone.

This is familiar to you: one of those trick situations life positively loves to trap you in. You remember, for instance, that time you and X had arranged to meet late afternoon at the entrance to the Design Show and go in together. You showed up: no X. From snatches of conversation overheard as you loitered by the door, you figured out there was *another* entrance at the other end of the vast exhibit hall. And right away, you broke out in a cold sweat. What if X was waiting at that other entrance, wondering where the heck you were? Maybe you'd better go and see? But then again, what if you really were supposed to meet up at the entrance where you are right now, and X shows up right when you head out looking for him? Or worse yet: X is in fact waiting for you at the other entrance. But while you're on your way there, rounding the enormous exhibit hall, he has the same thought you did. He heads out to find you at the entrance you just left, rounding the building on the opposite side, so that neither of you are any closer to finding each other—you've just swapped places. (What actually happened was the jovial X popped up behind you just then, shouting "Yoo-hoo!" and putting an end to this awkward dilemma.)

So, fine—you've always made mountains out of molehills. Finding a space in an airport parking structure often takes longer than you think, even this early in the morning. Same goes for waiting on your luggage at the carousel—it's like your suitcase always takes an impish pleasure in being among the last to emerge from the conveyor belt. You probably have a few minutes to go grab some coffee. If by some extraordinary chance A and B should turn up, separately or both at once, from the two opposite poles where you situate them in your head—A from the parking structure and B from beyond the sliding doors where the first few travelers are just starting to trickle out—well, they're not stupid. They'll figure you can't have gone far, maybe you went to the restroom, for instance, and they'll wait for you to come back. One thing's for sure: the longer you spend dithering, the bigger the chance the exact situation you fear most will arise. If you're going to make up your mind, make it up *now*.

Done! You're off! There you are, hurrying across the terminal all the way to the coffee shop, where—you didn't plan for this—no less than four people are already waiting in line. Don't get upset. Don't keep checking your watch every five seconds. At least this gives you time to examine, with a discerning eye, the wizened pastries on display behind the glass counter—maybe you'll just stick to coffee after all. Service seems unbelievably slow. The little old lady two ahead of you in line spends a significant amount of time looking for her change purse and extracting the price of her purchase coin by coin. Christ, could they get a move on? Can't they see the clock's ticking, and you have to dash back to the other end of the airport? A and B are surely there now, and what if they decided to go look for you by the restrooms? Your turn at last. You order. The placid arrogance with which the cashier announces the exorbitant price of your coffee fills your head with fleeting thoughts of murder. You should have known better; you've been in enough airports, and yet this organized extortion still manages to outrage you. No, don't get started. Just pay, turn around without a word, and head back across the terminal, fast. Not that fast! Try not spilling your coffee, that'd just make your day.

Hurrying nonetheless, you return to the spot you started from. During your absence—longer than you'd hoped—the aspect of the place has slowly changed. A growing number of visitors are now clustered along the security railing. Before them, the frosted glass doors slide open at a more regular pace than before, letting out travelers dragging small suitcases along or pushing baggage carts before them. Cries of recognition, waves hello, reunions with hugs and kisses. Other travelers have no one waiting, and dash off in search of a taxi. Despite the intermittency of these comings and goings, the number of elements comprising this subset of humanity remains more or less stable, each element (or group of elements) n that leaves soon replaced by an equivalent quantity n'—a curious Brownian motion that would, in other circumstances, be fascinating to study. But that's not why you're here. Your gaze sweeps the crowd several times looking for two precise quantities: but there isn't the slightest trace of A, and still no B. This time, you start worrying in earnest. How can A not be here yet? Even if he had to circle several times and go up several floors to find a spot, he should already be right here beside you. Right away, you start coming up with the worst disaster scenarios. The car broke down all of a sudden. The cars behind it let out a horn concerto. Their drivers got out, fit to be tied, and then, figuring out what had happened, changed their tune and helped him push the vehicle out of the way: a happy ending. Or maybe A got in a shouting match with another driver who'd snaked a spot right out from under him. They came to blows, and A got his face beaten in. Or maybe he had a heart attack—really, what nonsense is this? Besides, there he is! Crap, it's not him, just someone who looks oddly like him. (Actually, no, he looks nothing like him at all.) Meanwhile, what's taking B so long? From having waited so long at the carousel, now empty but still going round and round, B has resigned himself to the inevitable: his suitcase is lost, on a transatlantic flight to Mexico at this very moment—that is, if it ever left the ground to begin with. He's busy filling out piles of paperwork at the lost luggage desk. Or he's recovered his suitcase, but before takeoff some drug dealer slipped a kilo of heroin inside that some baggage handler was supposed to grab on arrival but couldn't, you read about something like that recently online. So the cops collared B, dragged him in cuffs to a dark hole where they're busy smacking him upside the head with a phone book right now to make him talk...

Will you get real for a second? Let A make his endless rounds of the parking structure and concentrate on B. He might in fact be held up on the other side by a persnickety customs officer. But it's likelier he came through the door while you were waiting in line for coffee. He knows his plane was really late, but doesn't know you weren't on time either, that at this very moment A's still trying to park (if he's not in an ambulance on the way to the hospital... no, don't start that again). What probably popped into his head was this: you decided to wait for him over a hot cup of coffee. And while you were waiting here, he went to look for you at the coffee shop. Simultaneously, your trajectories described two parabolas in opposite directions, or maybe your paths crossed but you didn't see each other: hardly surprising, what with all those people wandering around and your way of staring at the ground when you walk. Well—what now? At this point, why not go back there and take a look? At least moving around might help you calm down.

On the way, you come up with another scenario. What if B had missed his plane? He wouldn't have wanted to call you up and tell you in the middle of the night. Taking the time difference into account, he would've figured out roughly when you'd wake up—except he was an hour off. Maybe at this very moment, in the living room of your apartment, his message is making the light on your answering machine blink red.

Here you are again, in front of the coffee shop. And no B, of course. But really, you expected as much. Coming back here was a mistake; why do you always make such bad decisions? In the meantime, A's surely turned up at the other end of the airport looking for you, with no idea what's going on. Or B's come through the sliding doors, can't see either one of you, and is taken aback. Or even this: A and B have found each other, and set out in search of you, but in the opposite direction.

As you head back across the terminal, you wonder if you're making the wrong decision yet again. For supposing that A and B have indeed met up and set out looking for you, shouldn't you stay right where you are and not budge an inch? "If you're lost, stay where you are"—isn't that what they tell children? (But which one of you three is lost? That is, perhaps, the real question, which you will later return to consider: this is no time for philosophizing.) Sure, but what if at this very moment, A and B, separately or both at once, are reaching the same conclusion? You're not all going to stay where you are at different ends of the airport waiting for the other two to come, are you?

Now you're more undecided than ever. You wish you could split yourself in two: one self to head back and wait for B, the other self to make a beeline for the parking structure, since something serious might actually have happened to A, or at least something unanticipated. But even splitting in two wouldn't be enough; you'd need one more self to keep hanging out at the coffee shop and, why not, another self to take a taxi home to see if there's a message on the machine.

Your steps have automatically brought you back toward the middle of the airport. From there, you could continue in a straight line to where the travelers are coming out, with the risk that A could be waiting for you by the ladies' room while B is looking for you at the coffee shop. Or you could see what's going on in the parking structure, while A is in fact waiting in line to buy coffee for all of you while B, having at long last recovered his suitcase and overcome the customs officials' suspicion, emerges exhausted from the sliding glass doors. Or you could stay right where you are, while A lies dying from cardiac arrest on the parking structure's cold cement floor and B, having missed his plane, is waiting in another airport for the next flight to your city. You reflect that, all in all, you, A, and B, make up the three points of an infinitely variable triangle. Each of your movements alters the position of the other two accordingly: your partner A and your dear friend B. But if you stop, they'll stop too, one way or another. And when you retrace your steps, they will head off in the opposite direction. With the three of you moving every which way, perhaps the triangle you form will shrink enough for this no-exit set-up to end happily: you might reasonably expect to finally catch a glimpse of one another in the distance, then converge simultaneously toward a central point, *T*, which will mark the spot of your reunion, your hugs and kisses. But on the other hand, perhaps you are condemned to remain equidistant from each other and go round in circles indefinitely, in an airport that keeps filling and emptying itself of travelers both leaving and newly arrived, of friends and family come to see them off, or welcome them home. ◆

James D'Agostino

ATTENTION SURPLUS DISORDER

Catatonia, I'm onto
you. It's not I can't be told

a story to believe. It's broken

ice on the river somehow
reflects more sun than

fell just then. Again, I'm sorry.
What did that sound you said

say? Are the last grafts

of ancient wallpaper your
favorite part of attics or not?

Or the roof nails pounded through?
Is it me or does the moon seem

rounder in a blue sky? If you
can fall apart can't you stack

back some of it? There
must be something smart to
sing today. I'm a fool at school

and I'm no poem at home but
still try to say so and stay. Some

nights now I slacken, glance
back at my sack of day's

misspeech, beseech some
busted uncle up there strengthen
me to do the tighten up tomorrow.

Most I just do sorrow. I do a different
light left on or off or I do less

than I can go into. I do lists of
have to, lists of screw you

and the month slumps along,
humps its everyday freight of giddy
and shitty. Some of it's semblable

in the semi-babble, but really,
the sphere of the said's small,

tear-soluable and of interest only
to those with some love song

aplomb to blubber from
and tons of ice and rum,
gibbering slipperier fixatives

into this flux all us lummox must
just lust for sorely. Just look at us.

Mississippi
Review

send your

barbaric yawp

to our annual contest

info@

mississippireview.com

Austin R. Pick

THE ACQUISITIONS DEPARTMENT

He was thinking about boxes inside boxes, sensing suddenly that the rectangular conference room he was sitting in possessed the same proportions of length and width as the sheet of paper in his hands. He noticed too that the triad of cubed windows alongside the door were themselves frosted with tiny squares of translucent glass, like a screen of pixels that revealed or reflected only shifting blocks of light and shadow, from either side.

Alone in the rectangular room, the words danced in meaningless strings as he held the page before him. He'd been left here following his first interview, and simply instructed to wait. It seemed as if time were unfolding on some mythic scale, and the paper struck him as at once precious and irrelevant: his résumé, confined to a single sheet, with his name across the top in a distinctive font, which itself had a name he couldn't now recall.

There was also the conference table at which he sat, an oblong suspended lid the color of old plasticware. It seemed to share its size with the closed door of the room, which was heavy, dark, and had sealed sometime ago with a pneumatic gasp, as if hermetically. He could lie flat on the table, he imagined, and not dangle. Invisible beneath him, his feet felt lost somewhere down in the vaulted shaft of the building, wavering indeterminately in the cold unseen heights of the glass reception hall, perhaps, dozens of floors below.

Flush with morning sun when he'd entered, the reception hall comprised the entire ground floor, where the building's entrances gave way to the rectilinear expanse of the main lobby. Approaching the elevator banks across a broad tiled floor, his steps had been muffled by an echo that made every sound seem distant. The hall was like being inside an enormous display case, he'd thought, and exhibited to the rushing intersections outside, where sidewalks treadmilled under the syncopation of swinging briefcases and hands hailing cabs as people hurried in all four directions on their way to work.

Elevators plunging upward, reaching toward this closed conference room from the paned glass lobby of a building occupying a single square block in a city structured on a grid. Boxes inside boxes. He felt his stomach drop, thinking about it.

Hours earlier, the H.R. Assistant had said his name wrong when greeting him as he was ejected from the elevator, pronouncing it by stressing the "v" in a voice like honeyed toast, easy and edged. "Mr. Uhverman, I'm Leslie Spinner," she said, stiffly extending her hand.

"It's *Averman*," he replied, emphasizing the initial vowel as he took her hand briefly, "and please, call me Daniel." He'd intended to introduce himself differently, more deferentially, and blanched at having corrected her. She was just *there*, as the elevator opened, poised and quite striking in a jacket and matching pants, waiting for him.

He'd imagined having to do the waiting himself, with a little time, perhaps behind a magazine, to rewire the fragile network of nerves stitching together his sense of self—a cellular procession that was finely lined, it felt like, with the itchy tangle of self-description he'd been rehearsing. He was early, after all. But he was also, he reflected, *expected*. He'd signed in down in the lobby, and had changed elevators once in a kind of vertical commute he'd already decided, anticipating a question, that yes, he could certainly get used to.

Just remember to breathe, he encouraged himself, nostrils filling with a shrill whistle as he straightened his lapels and stretched his lips into a grin. She smiled in return as the elevator chimed shut behind him, and lit her eyes with decisive kindness. Probably, he speculated, reading his thoughts. He attempted a blank slate, mentally. Still, some combination of growing hunger and a sudden, constricting lust for this bloused and burnished woman made him a little dizzy, a confused aggregation of basic needs surging inside him—primal, cave-dwelling instincts that were instead blandly transmuted into these ingratiating niceties and a cheap haircut. He wished he'd managed to eat breakfast.

"It's nice to meet you, Daniel," she replied, with convincing sincerity. "You're scheduled for two interviews today, for a position in the Acquisitions Department. Please, follow me." She said it like a question, and Daniel stiffened against his immediate impulse to comply.

During his phone evaluation two weeks ago, the tactful ambiguity of her voice had made it difficult to assess whether he was being taken seriously or not. Her tone was clipped and businesslike, and as he'd paced around in his pajamas, straining to condense the better elements of his personality into an articulate, modest confidence, Daniel had been free to imagine the woman on the other end of the line dismally rolling her eyes, filing her nails with one of those little wands, making exaggerated gagging gestures or otherwise silently broadcasting her disinterest to an entire mutely snickering Human Resources team.

As he stood grinning outside the elevator, however, the incongruity of meeting her and finding this almost disarming sense of pleasantness put Daniel in the awkward position of not being sure whom to distrust more, himself or her. For him, it was a familiar dilemma.

Spooled in cascading ringlets, her hair was all curls as she turned, and Daniel nearly tripped over his wingtips as he followed her down a broad hallway. The space was permeated with her perfume, a scratchy and oddly alluring scent that reminded him of dried flowers and insecticide. His eyes cursored along the blank walls and waffle-patterned ceiling tiles, folder flapping in one hand while he brushed himself with the other, discretely checking his fly as she briskly led him past the hushed glass doors of various departments, each labeled with weird acronyms and hyphenated digits.

She didn't offer any explanation as Daniel trailed after her along a convoluted series of narrow corridors, punctuated only by the occasional closed door. "Did you have any difficulty getting here?" she asked him instead, turning slightly to speak over her shoulder.

Daniel answered amiably that it had been easy to find the appropriate floor, even while prefiguring a response, somewhere within his anxious interior, to the broader dimension of her question, thinking that at a quick count he had, over the past nine or so months, trolled job-posting sites almost hourly and submitted his résumé with accompanying cover letters to nearly a hundred different companies; clicked and typed through at least a dozen online applications and recruiting sites; taken basic aptitude assessments for six staffing agencies; completed three rigorous personality profiles and twice agreed to possible drug testing; applied to be an experimental study subject and then been screened out because he was left-handed; lived under his parent's roof without accountable means of supporting himself other than his ability to walk the dog, mow the grass, and empty the dishwasher, none of which any of the neighbors were willing to pay him to do, despite the distribution of printed flyers and a "pay what you will" scheme; applied for another deferment on the student loans that had loomed darkly for several years, and subverted his now vague aspirations in a job search that had netted him exactly two phone interviews and one legitimate callback to date, this one—thinking well yes, you could say he'd faced some challenges in getting here, but the commute had gone smoothly and the train wasn't too badly overrun with vagrants or their lingering odor this morning, thank you.

Straining against his suit seams, Daniel tried slowing to approximate her toned composure. *Professional*, he was thinking, savoring the word's tensile strength and slipping it cape-and-cowl-like over an imagined image of himself, smartly dressed and smoothly striding, *professional and punctual. This candidate*, he continued, watching her walk, *is highly motivated, adept at unraveling complications and meeting difficult deadlines.* It was fortifying to envision himself assessing her, rather than the other way around. Her every movement suggested the practiced bearing of pageants and runways, calculated posturing and mechanical hand waving, legs like flashing scissor blades in their pointed heels.

These observations formed brief eddies among his turbid and skittish thoughts, but despite murmuring appreciably at regular intervals, Daniel was having trouble following the thread of what she was actually saying. As she bounded along, habitually twisting to glance at her little wristwatch, he was beginning to think she might be better described as *work-obsessed and high-strung*, when Ms. Spinner finally slowed before a double door of glass, brushing back an errant curl as she swiped her security pass. "I'm sorry if I've gotten you turned around," she said. "It's easy to get lost up here." Daniel nodded dumbly.

"Actually, I'm enjoying the tour," he said, forcing a smile and reaching to hold the door for her. Assuming he hadn't sounded sarcastic, Daniel congratulated himself for being *personable*, and followed her into a cavernous office space, bright with noise. He was finally in, he realized, with an outside chance of actually getting the job, whatever that meant.

Ms. Spinner retrieved a thick binder from another assistant as she led him through the inner office, accepting it like a relay baton. "I'm sorry if things seem rushed," she said, cradling the binder and riffling its pages as she continued to walk. Daniel noticed the age her voice betrayed, and cringed at his initial impulse to undress her. "We have a large number of applicants to see, and as I mentioned, our process is quite comprehensive." Did she mention that? He strained to remember what she'd been saying before, uneasy about what else he might have missed.

Daniel caught himself squinting a little, as if trying to see down the tangle of hallways they'd just walked, and admitted that he couldn't possibly retrace his steps back to the elevators. "I understand," he offered doubtfully, musing that this must be the physical endurance part of the evaluation. His eyes were stinging from the air conditioning or dehydration, probably both. And while he knew he should be thinking of this as a *valuable learning experience*, he couldn't help entertaining the bleak notion that it was all just a hallucinated metaphor for the indefinite direction of his life. He tried to think of something intelligent to ask, but kept anticipating the answers to his own questions, or wondering about things he should already know, like what the hell Acquisitions was, anyway.

They passed a workspace where hunched employees sat cloistered within a stockade of filing cabinets, and Daniel saw three men, each older than the last, sitting in a row. Glimpsing them peripherally between the shelves, he had the impression of seeing a single person's life in time-lapse, stooped before the same unblinking screen. For an instant he couldn't believe he'd ever actually choose to work here, but acknowledged, in the same moment, that it wasn't really his choice at all. He noticed that there was also an apparently empty desk in the row, suggesting an open position. His panic had downshifted into an optimistic paranoia of some kind, and he was no longer so anxious now, merely suspicious of every subtext, watching for signs like a malnourished mystic. He thought he might faint.

Already famished, he imagined himself deflating when he next sat down, leaving his empty suit draped like a wrinkled pelt. The interview had already begun, he realized suddenly, seized by a prickling surge of preparatory advice, and he was being assessed even now, challenged to *take the initiative* and somehow *distinguish himself* from a throng of other applicants, whose thin résumés were crowding the desks of every interviewer in the city, an entire population reduced to flimsy black-and-white photocopies.

"I have copies of my résumé right here," Daniel announced, hoisting his folder with an assertive flourish. He was buoyed briefly by the thought of those crisp sheets of premium-weight paper, his name emblazoned across the top in a carefully chosen font. All at once he felt desperately confident, and hoped reproachfully that he hadn't sounded too arrogant.

The H.R. Assistant ignored him as they turned before a large wall bearing the company's familiar logo, swirling stylized clouds flanking a lightning bolt whose jagged edges suggested the lines on a stock chart or EKG reading. Daniel found it suddenly disorienting to be *inside* a corporation whose ubiquitous presence radiated diffuse power around the globe, this same austere logo everywhere beaming wordless omniscience from the great heights of buildings and billboards. He felt drained, exhausted by incessant urgency.

Inscrutable in her self-assurance, Ms. Spinner stopped before a half-open door and gestured for him to enter. Inside the narrow office a woman rose to greet them, so similar in dress and demeanor that, to Daniel's eye, the two could have been sisters. "Ms. Parcell, this is Mr. Uhverman," the H.R. Assistant said, getting his name wrong again. He didn't correct her, but simply introduced himself as Daniel. The woman's hand felt cold and brittle, but her thin smile revealed a shrewdness that Daniel took as an encouragement or a challenge. He was here for an *interview*, he remembered, and turned to thank Ms. Spinner as she briskly excused herself, already oblivious of him.

Daniel adjusted his awkwardly knotted tie as if to truss himself up. The walls were the same clammy shades he'd seen elsewhere, but here there was an earnest overlay of decoration, with framed images of old maps, a large, luridly green imitation plant, and a woven rug atop the stiff carpet beneath them. The woman's desk was adorned with a tableau of scattered antiques, including an abacus and an old folding ruler. The office seemed like a stock facsimile of corporate success, and struck Daniel as having the same forced serenity of a funeral parlor. He mumbled a compliment anyway, hoping to spark some warmth or affinity in the frigid space, but felt exposed sitting there, his confidence condensed along a narrow ledge, his balance unsteady.

He swallowed dryly and looked the woman over while she sat reading his résumé, preparing to take measure of him. There was something spare about her, despite the shoulder pads, and she was older than Ms. Spinner, with silver hair pulled back in a single braid. Her small face had a pinched angularity that suggested habitual vigilance, and though she was apparently calm, her neck and jaw were clenched and taut, as if prefiguring a grimace. Her fingers rasped softly on the desk as she read, the nail of her index finger much longer than the others—a honed scalpel, Daniel guessed, for dissecting stacked files and forms.

Why hadn't they at least offered him water? Scanning the room for a basket or bowl of anything edible, he gathered that employers, like airlines, were no longer offering snacks. Daniel decided his first question was going to be about where all the vending machines were. These little inward jokes of his seemed increasingly edged, like sharks' fins circling any tenuous, foundering surety that might remain. He sometimes privately sensed, with a deep unease bordering on awe, that the entire world was animated solely by ceaseless hunger, the keen appetites of lean beasts and the ten thousand indiscriminate cravings of his own kind, cleanly packaged and politely purposed, but seething always with need.

His stomach was a pothole, swallowing itself. He'd been too nervous to eat anything this morning, which now made him nervous about his ability to form complete sentences. Each ticking second seemed precipitous, his chances receding across the apportioned void of occupied office cubes, not a single square left open for him. He had to get this job. Had to. His whole life was on hold, and he was penniless, his options exhausted, left friendless as those he'd known vanished into a similar anonymity, Daniel himself stranded in a panicked stasis that amounted to failure without ever having the opportunity to try. He knew that another office job, with its tedious routines and quotidian belittlements, wouldn't solve every equation, but what alternative did he have right now, in this economy? Flip burgers? Grow his own food? Criticisms of the so-called "rat race" seemed more and more to him like the ungrateful grumblings of the comfortable, mumbled between mouthfuls of cheese.

He straightened up and folded his hands together, doing his best to adopt a sense of ready patience. *I'm the one you're looking for,* he intoned silently, hoping to sway her psychically or at least improve his own demeanor, *and I'm available to start immediately.* Inspecting herself with a downward glance, Ms. Parcell plucked at a loose thread on her suit jacket, unraveling it a little and giving a decisive pull before discreetly tucking it away, still unbroken. She looked up then and introduced herself as the H.R. Coordinator. "So tell me about yourself, Daniel," she said after a pause. He flushed hotly. *Well, I've been looking for a job for about as long as I can remember, and that's about it,* was his first thought. He dreaded open-ended introductions, and fought to recall anything he'd rehearsed.

Just condense your life into a single, charming-as-hell sentence, he coached himself miserably, blinking back against the pressure at his temples. Why did she think he was here? Hadn't she *just* read his résumé? It was probably a setup. She'd already hired someone, and was only humoring him. He was definitely overreacting. *Just say something.*

"My name is Daniel Averman," he said finally, declaratively, "and I think one of my most important attributes, which may not come across in my résumé, is that I'm adaptable. I'm able to conform myself to the demands of the task at hand." Surprising himself, he hoped the words, when spoken, would be self-fulfilling. He sensed that he was being prompted to reveal a store of hidden deficiencies, and that she would next ask him to specify his weaknesses, another question he openly feared. Instead, she'd just begun to say something when the phone rang.

Ms. Parcell turned aside and lifted the receiver, her expression crystalizing as she listened. Daniel watched as she rapidly aged before him, truly scowling now, whether from hostility or some stark, executive logic, her skull swelling under the skin of her face, gone sallow. Looking in his direction, looking at the prospect, but not the person of him, she absently drew her single long fingernail across her throat, articulating a precise, deliberate line that terminated with a snap of the wrist, as if she were making a note to herself.

"I'm sorry, but we're going to have to cut this short," she said, turning toward Daniel again after murmuring into the phone, her face recomposing around the blank screens of her eyes, dark in their sockets, her fingers methodically straightening the tangled cord as she spoke. Something *urgent* and *requiring immediate attention.* He stared at her, stunned.

"Ms. Parcell, please, let me have just a moment more. I'm a self-starter with robust interpersonal skills and an aptitude for problem solving," Daniel croaked, stringing together a slack high wire of stock phrases, memorized in their endless iterations. "With a professionalism marked by an enjoyment of challenges and team-spirited independence," he continued, feeling increasingly vaporous as he obsequiously rambled on, vestiges of his threadbare dignity unraveling with every breath. Eventually he trailed off, void of any residual anger and utterly resigned, shrinking under the scrutiny of her fixed gaze.

Ms. Parcell remained motionless, but regarded him intensely, her thin smile etched now with interest, with what Daniel could only describe as ruthless amusement, a strange light returning to her eyes. "You seem to be settling in here already, Daniel, and I believe you'll do just fine," she intoned, "but it's not entirely my decision to make. Now, if you'll excuse me." Her assessment apparently complete, she left Daniel to show himself out.

He didn't know whether to feel relieved or humiliated when the interview abruptly ended—some unseen, inexorable power shearing away his already grim prospects with a simple phone call. Ms. Spinner retrieved him from the hallway and explained that they were next headed upstairs to Acquisitions, where Daniel was scheduled for a meeting with the department supervisor. He said nothing as she led him on to a different bank of elevators, where they plunged rapidly upward to an equally indistinct floor.

Turning further into the convoluted maze, Ms. Spinner brought him at last to the rectangular conference room, lights flickering haltingly as she waved him inside. They were early for his next interview, she informed him, the door already closing, and he would have to wait here. She left without another word, and Daniel slumped into a chair, withdrawing a copy of his résumé and letting the folder fall limply to the table, the paper at once precious and irrelevant, summarizing a self that seemed remote and increasingly fictional.

The walls of the conference room warped around him, and his résumé felt elastic as he held it in both hands. Blearily, Daniel began to discern the suggestion of a barcode in the blockish pattern of abstracted black against the white of the page, and turned the sheet sideways to further induce the effect. He envisioned himself lying on the table with the résumé affixed to his chest, ready to be registered by the unseen machinery of the company and assigned a small salary and the coördinates to a desk, somewhere definite down below.

Turning the page to restore its conformity with the room's proportions, Daniel gauged that he'd been here for hours now, nearly a quarter of a day, twelve thousand seconds and counting. He'd tried to stop keeping track, tried to convince himself that he couldn't remember when he'd been left alone here, to wait. Though unnerved by the ghostly display showing the time, he'd checked his phone repeatedly, puzzling over the oddity of an office building with no reception and wondering if it was somehow intentional, or merely the result of mercurial service— a dead zone for him alone.

He'd deliberated every explanation, seeking some course of action, and realized that the evaluation might still be unfolding even now, testing his patience and endurance, or perhaps his assertiveness and ingenuity. The interview process, it seemed, had somehow become an initiation. He could leave the room and seek someone out, but risked being presumptuous, or getting lost, or becoming an object of ridicule, none of which seemed to accord with the patterns of a place where everything was accounted for. He imagined slowly unraveling the fabric of his necktie and creating a guideline like a lost cave explorer, but dismissed the thoughts as they arose, recognizing their futility.

Daniel had encountered increasingly desperate strategies during his months of job searching. A man standing on a street corner and handing out copies of his résumé to anyone, it seemed, who made eye contact with him and was wearing a tie. A woman advertising herself on a billboard with a large, postured portrait and a tagline in fanciful script that read something like, "Seeking excellence in an employer," her contact details emphasizing the whites of her eyes as she stared out over the ash-gray expressway. Seeing the billboard, Daniel had pictured her at a kitchen table shrouded in evening gloom, figuring the cost of the ad against her savings and the stock in her pantry. He'd almost called to ask if she'd had any offers, and perhaps by extension a forecast for him too.

To him these attempts were all inflected with a tinge of gimmickry, though he couldn't be sure he wasn't simply envious. His own efforts, it seemed, amounted to relinquishing everything unique about himself, given over to the common denominator as he squeezed ever further into an unyielding box. Outside on the streets even now, those who refused the same contortions were banging drums and shouting up at the implacable facades, but still affirming, in their protest, the same powers that Daniel was halfheartedly imploring.

The room's wavering solidity was stretched taut along every line, attuned to the finest vibration of breath or movement, and his own body was like putty, held in shape only by the strictures of his clothing and the contoured hollowness of his hunger. Was he being watched? He pictured his inquisitors, assuming the third would look similar, if more severe, and wondered if they were meeting now, gathered around a monitor, taking measure of him. He remained still, sensing the dimensions of his solitude. He would wait for some conclusion, for three women in pantsuits to decide his fate.

Somehow, almost obstinately, he refused to believe he'd been forgotten. Whatever the logic of his isolation, he would wait, demonstrating forbearance and what he hoped would resemble equanimity. If necessary, he would remain until employment became inevitable, until he was absorbed by default into the operations of the company. He would give himself over, his ill-fitting suit squaring his shoulders as he sat within a shrinking room in a building occupying an entire block of a city splayed on a grid, boxes inside boxes, closing in.

The page felt warm in his hands, the texture of the premium-weight paper like the skin of a peach. Each sentence was carefully worded and every paragraph justified to form a procession of compressed, evenly aligned rectangles—the sum of his assessable life stacked like a pile of squashed cars in a salvage lot. He had stared at his résumé until it had lost all meaning, the white flashing before his eyes, the text darkly shifting shapes in silhouette. He'd selected an eco-stock when getting them printed, he remembered, made from soy ink and recycled vegetation. The fibers seemed to bulge now under his thumbs, the veined remainder of banana leaves, pressed and woven into paper.

Almost imperceptibly, Daniel began to salivate; he then impulsively tore at a corner, pulling away a thin strip across the bottom of the page. The sound of the ripping was delicious, like butter sizzling in a pan. He placed the end of the strip on his tongue and slowly drew it in, slurping as if it were a strand of spaghetti. He imagined cream sauce as he chewed, fastidiously pulping the strip and reaching to tear off another. He stuffed a slim list of his skills and abilities into his mouth, thinking of thick-cut steak fries as he consumed his early internships and previous employment in little slivers, absorbed now and chewing studiously. The effort was tiring, and he began to pace himself after half a page or so, methodically chomping on savory morsels of cubed beef, the paper squelching between his teeth. It was *lean and fortifying*, his résumé, an offering of himself as sustenance.

As he made a salad of small pieces and scooped a fistful, it occurred to him that by rationing his remaining copies, he could remain indefinitely, absolved of all identity and ready, at last, to be assimilated. Reaching the top of the page, he gulped down his education history in a neatly curled spring roll. The black marks of his name evoked the charred scores on grilled chicken, and Daniel relaxed as he swallowed that too, sitting folded in the chair and listening for any sound beyond the walls that might offer some portent. As ever, it was quiet. The building's silent totality engulfed him—spooled out, measured, and finally severed from the distinctions that had etched his sense of self in that fragile network of text, realigning his proportions to fit within the vast anonymous architecture of the company, incorporating him cell by cell. He would wait. Soon doors would open, documents would be signed, and the acquisition would be complete. He would wait. ✦

Rachel X. Weissman

I WANT YOU

My father collects music on reel-to-reel tapes. I love the elaborate threading of the stainless-steel player, the tape passing through spindles guiding it to a magnetic head that decodes the sound. At five years old, I think him a wizard, controlling this machine that fills our subway-car-sized living room with the melancholy notes of Bach's Unaccompanied Cello Suites and the crackling precision of the Well-Tempered Clavier.

He sets his Pall Mall in the triangular yellow-and-white Cinzano ashtray that my mother pocketed from a restaurant on one of our European holidays. I watch his strong hands, his thumbs chewed raw on the sides near the nail.

Daddy, let me.

He wraps my small fingers around the tape and helps me thread it through the spindles. I glance up at his crooked smile, his uncombed hair, sticking out from the sides of his head like blades of a drunken windmill, and inhale the musty smell from the darkroom where he's been developing prints. Warmth spreads up from my chest, tingling my scalp.

A few years later, I'll start music lessons, and though I lack discipline, my recorder teacher tells me I excel at Bach. His simple arpeggiated melodies express ecstasy, sorrow, and grief. Grand emotions I sense are part of the grown-up world I will someday inhabit.

2

I'm so spooked in general and afraid of sharks in particular—years before the release of "Jaws"—that I worry about being attacked, even while taking a bath. My father buys me a small mechanical dolphin for protection. It swims in the tub, towing its pup behind, and every twenty seconds or so spouts water from a blowhole.

Once protected by the dolphin, I take long, steaming-hot baths, rocking forward and back, the water sloshing within the tub as though a tidal wave were threatening my personal body of water on Manhattan's Upper West Side. Or as though I were a piece of photographic paper, my story developing on my naked body.

I love watching him work in his darkroom, using a tool that resembles an eye patch attached to a piece of wire. Like a sun god, my father blocks the light from the enlarger, dappling the image of a man in negative on a London street. More miraculous still is when he gently shakes the plastic tray of "magic water" in which floats an 8×10, the positive image of the man creeping onto the paper, like a message from another world.

3

My great-aunt Minnie and grandmother on my father's side run a thrift store in Times Square that—as family lore tells it—is frequented by prostitutes and transvestites. Minnie presents me with clothes that my mother believes come from *the store*. Arriving in plastic dry cleaner bags, they reek of Estée Lauder bath oil, the elixir my great aunt uses as perfume. The clothes seem grown-up and hip, nothing like what my mother buys me. *Teens on "American Bandstand" wear stuff like this*, I think when admiring the short tweed purple-and-blue shirtdress with gold buttons running its length. I beg my mother for a pair of white patent-leather go-go boots to wear with the dress. She refuses, saying that white patent leather is too tacky.

My mother is "classy," her only makeup a splash of red lipstick, her style casual and unadorned. Her dramatic salt-and-pepper hair is cut short, and once a man on the street told her she looked like Patricia Nixon, which flattered her even if the politics were off. Later, my father tells me he always wanted to be my mother, that he married his ideal self.

The present Aunt Minnie gives me when I turn eight is nothing my mother can complain about. The small black AM transistor radio bewitches me and I listen to it constantly. I shiver to the simple, legato tones of the vibraphone in the bridge of the Stylistics' "Break Up to Make Up." The lyrics make me think of my parents at cocktail hour, the times when my dad's voice gets loud and my mom's takes on that edge that says whatever he's done is not okay and can't be undone. The times when he stomps off and slams the hallway door, trailed by her angry and disappointed *Oh, Marty*. My mother is "bourgeois," I hear him tell a friend on the phone. *He never tells me what he's feeling*, I hear my mother tell one of hers.

Sometimes I sleep with the little black box beneath my pillow. One Sunday morning, I wake with my chest constricted by anxiety, not knowing where I am. *Ground Control to Major Tom*, a voice says from beneath my pillow. The voice is David Bowie's, tense with claustrophobia and despair. I clench my blanket as he tells the story of an astronaut in a space capsule spun out of control. Something in his tone tells me this song is not just about Major Tom, that it's about me and my mom and my dad and everyone I know, spinning and alone and lonely.

4

I sit on the radiator cover in my bedroom, the window cracked, smoking cigarettes, burning incense, wondering when my life will start. Bored, frustrated, and strangely excited by the glimmerings of an adult world that feels just out of reach, impossible for my thirteen-year-old body to inhabit.

My mother knocks.

What do you want?

I just want to know how you are. May I come in?

Don't open the door. I'm fine. Go away. Each word a dagger.

Poor woman: she is petrified by the bristling teenager I've become.

My father has vacated our Upper West Side apartment, moving to a loft downtown. My parents are separated; I wear this new status like a war medal.

Your father and I just can't live with each other anymore. It happens sometimes. How do you feel about this?

Oh Christ, not this again.

Sent to a shrink, I spend my time observing the objects in the room, noticing the changing location of the orange ceramic rooster from the table to the windowsill.

At first my father's leaving unmoors me, my love for him so much simpler than my love for my mother. But soon I learn that more attention is to be had from him in this new dual-household situation. Besides, myriad routes to escape adult surveillance emerge.

One day I cut school to lose my virginity with Bobby, the hand-me-down boyfriend I inherited from my prettier and more popular best friend. Years before Nike, I live their slogan: Just do it. I concoct a plan to transport myself and my circle of five close girlfriends to the other side of the chasm that separates us from adulthood: each of us must lose our virginity before turning fourteen. Misguided attempts at conquering my fears by diving into shallow water characterize much of the next twenty years of my life.

Bobby is super cool and the perfect prospect. A few years older than me, he rides a skateboard, is a low-echelon graffiti writer, has longish dirty-blond hair and a nasty scar on his neck. The "quick-come kid," he proudly calls himself, and I so ignorant as to believe it a lofty title. He's dropped LSD hundreds of times, and when we trip together he becomes a cartoon character, spewing the phrase "Tripping, zipping, whoopie!" over and over, his face lit up by a manic smile.

The sex is anticlimactic, to say the least. It barely touches me emotionally or physically. A notch in my belt, a relief to have dispatched my virginity, leaving childhood behind. After, lying naked in bed in the guest room that was my father's darkroom before he left, I trace the raised, red scar that begins at Bobby's pale neck, ending at his bony hip.

How'd you get it?

He tells me he once dated a black girl, provoking an attack by racist thugs on a bridge.

I almost bled to death.

Then I know he's worthy of my attention. Sex becomes an opportunity to collect stories, experiences. My body and heart just hitchhikers on trips arranged by my destructive ambition.

5

I'm a woman trapped in a man's body.

My father's words don't make sense, don't jibe with the fifty-two-year-old man in a corduroy suit sitting across from me, whose head is balding in the middle, hair flying away on the sides.

I picture him years before, coming to see me on school days when I stayed home sick. Arriving from his workaday world, wearing his beige Burberry trenchcoat, to sit at my bedside, taking my face in his hands, as he does now.

Rachel, I'll always be your father, but this is something I feel inside.

I want to believe him, but his words ring false, as if he were auditioning for a part in a cheap TV movie.

I pull away.

This is so much more fucked up than anything I could have imagined. This reason for why my parents are divorcing. But part rings true; I've always felt something was wrong with him, with me. It must be something genetic, some strand of DNA twisted the wrong way that explains my sense of not fitting in with the kids at my junior high.

What do you mean? What does this mean: you're a man in a woman's body? Are you going to have an operation like that man in the magazine? I ask, recalling the *New York Times Magazine* story on Jan Morris from a few months before. Like a car wreck, it transfixed me and set me to wondering how I'd feel if this were ever to befall my family.

My father's hands are blurry with movement through my tears. They come toward me and pull back, unsure what to do. He pulls me to him and then I'm against his shoulder, the red and orange paisley pattern of his shirt filling my view.

No, no, shhhhhh, he whispers. *No, I won't have that operation. I'll always be your father.*

He lets go of me and takes from his pocket the stained handkerchief that I love because it is his imperfect and familiar object. Imperfect like us, tainted like us. He wipes my face with it, pressing too hard as usual, his expressions of physical affection earnest but always somewhat awkward. The roughness comforts me, even as I know nothing will ever be the same again.

6

When he told me, it felt like he stuck a knife inside my vagina and twisted it, my mother says.

Funny, I just feel numb.

My mother's rage overwhelms and surprises me, bursting from a Trojan horse, itsy-bitsy men brandishing spears, running round the room. I telescope her and the army into a small, manageable box, like the sign-language interpreter in the corner of a television screen.

I tell an older friend about my father. *He's not a freak*, she says. *No one is all male or all female, it's just a continuum. Don't worry.*

7

Two years pass. My father takes me to a small French restaurant in the West Village for a special occasion that will be a surprise. The room is elegant, suffused with a warm orangey light. I wear a lavender '40s dress bought for two dollars from a vintage store on his block, and he, his paisley Schiaparelli shirt.

Partway through, he leans forward to take my hand.

Bunny bear, remember when I told you about my feeling of being born in the wrong body?

Occasionally I wonder about the secret he shared with me. But mostly I don't think about it, nor about the "truth" I'd recognized about our freakishness.

I'm going through with it—with the operation.

The blood drains from my face.

You told me you would never have that operation. I focus on the smile lines etched at the corner of his eyes. *Dad, let's trip together. Cut through the veils of illusion, see who you really are.*

He smiles, considering my suggestion.

I tried smoking pot once, he offers. *I got so paranoid I thought the Nazis were after me. Besides, sweetheart, it's too late. I've started taking hormones.*

The waitress clears my half-finished dinner.

How can you be so sure? I'm never sure about anything. Trip with me.

She returns and reels off a list of desserts, ending with *crème brûlée.*

It's more than just hormones. The smile again. *I'm a eunuch. They cut my balls off.*

The rest of the surgery will take place in six months. That's when his penis will be cut off and a vagina synthesized for him.

I nod and smile until the waitress returns with my leftovers, beautifully wrapped in tin foil shaped into the form of a swan.

8

Why don't you get angry at him? my mother demands from the corner of my psychic TV screen.

How could he do this to me? To you, I mean.

You don't have to see him anymore.

Tell him to go fuck himself.

Ask him where the child support money is.

9

During the next few years, my father "transitions" from male to female. He takes hormones and sometimes wears women's clothes, two-piece suits he's sewed using inexpensive patterns purchased from Woolworth's. They are conservative in style but, like my father and his bohemian sensibilities, riddled with mistakes, sloppy hems, one lapel larger than the other. With his ratty wig, he looks like an awkward and eccentric Hasidic woman. The charade of femininity repels me: the artificially high and soft voice used to mask his true deep male voice, his attempts to bond with me over "women's issues" like menstruation. In public, I call him Mara, the name he's chosen for himself. But in private, I call him Dad. I hold him to his promise to always be my father.

10

SCENE: Graduation from my slacker high school. A crowd gathers on the steps outside, two retro hippies playing Frisbee in their midst.

BACKSTORY: A months-long argument between my mother and father about which one of them can attend. My mother will not go if *he's* there. He promises to stay away. But will he?

COSTUME: I'm wearing a floor-length black evening gown ($1.99 from the vintage clothing store bin), three sizes too big, pinned in the back.

ACTION: A few friends and I giggle and whisper as we leave the school building triumphant. I jump for the Frisbee coming at me, my gown falling to reveal a small, white breast. We do the female huddle, giggle-freak, and adjust the dress. And then I see him, skulking around the margins of the crowd. He's wearing Gucci.

My head tracks left and I make eye contact with my stricken mother, who turns to stare numbly at my father. He comes toward me and I take off.

MONTAGE SHOTS: My gown in hand as I speed across town. Through Father Demo Square, cutting around the fountain in Washington Square, past my father's building on Broadway, and by the great black cube at Astor Place. I end up in front of Freda's, the trannie bar, which guards the entrance to St. Mark's Place.

He's running after me, calling out my name, begging me to stop. Just as he arrives, I'm struck by the Third Avenue bus. Take that, Daddy.

DISCLOSURE: This is a fantasy.

11

My father's clients are baffled by his new identity. This is 1979, after all. His work as a photographer dries up and he moves from New York City to a small town in the Catskills. There he takes odd jobs that don't call on his skills as a photographer. As he settles into life upstate, he lets go of his notions of what a woman is and how she's supposed to act. At sixty years old, he returns to his old self—except for the wigs. His clothing no longer irks me; he dresses in jeans and boots. And while he's failed at forming romantic relationships, he's happy.

Once on a visit to a nearby mountaintop Tibetan monastery, we run into Ethel, an acquaintance of his who knows him as a woman. He introduces me to her as his daughter. We give her a ride to the village below. In the car, she attempts to lure me into conversation, mentioning this thing that "my mother" does and that thing that "my mother" does, imagining that I must be so proud of "my mother's" volunteer work at the crisis center. I bite my tongue in rage. I'd asked my father to introduce me as his niece to avoid just such a situation. Finally, pushed by one of her ceaseless idiotic questions, I snap, *He's not my mother.*

12

I take the red eye from Chicago to Mexico City to visit my father, who's begun spending winters in Pátzcuaro, a small town known mostly for producing oodles of Day of the Dead miniature statuary.

I should be leaving Chicago triumphant. At twenty-five, I've just had my first (and only) full-length play produced to good reviews and frequent sold-out audiences. My writing is taking some kind of public shape and I don't feel so cursed and different anymore. Though it seems miraculous that such a project has come to pass and is deemed a success, instead it's ruined for me because two people I respect criticized it. To make matters worse, on an ego high, I slept with several men in the theater troupe, feeling afterward empty and unsatisfied, talentless and unloved. No relationship approximates the intimacy my father and I share, an intimacy born from bearing the pain his choice inflicts on me.

He lives in a community of expats, self-titled Gringo Gulch. His little house with its roofless bathroom and a tree growing in its center charms me. Pátzcuaro is both beautiful and squalid, with a slaughterhouse dumping offal into the river running through its center. Rumor has it that the Army kills peasants, leaving their bodies along the roads, and that Lake Pátzcuaro is so polluted that a biologist studying it was taken to the hospital after dipping a cut finger into its waters.

Despite—or because of—this undercurrent of violence and peril, I'm transfixed by the devotion of the Catholic faithful. The Pope will be visiting Mexico City at Easter, a few months hence. A frenzy of pilgrims crosses the country on their knees to visit the Shrine of the Virgin of Guadalupe, Mexico's incarnation of Mary. The Virgin fascinates me, as do the beautiful churches she's inspired, churches that marry Catholicism and paganism, a syncretic religion, brilliant and merry but also tragic, its very existence a mark of conquest. We visit the Shrine of the Virgin, a weirdly modern chapel where I ride a moving walkway through the sacristy, beneath the patch of cloth that is to the cult of the Virgin what the Shroud of Turin is to Christianity.

My fascination entwines with the paradox of my father. He is strong; he is weak. He is masculine; he is feminine. He's carved out his own way in life; he's allowed a surgeon's knife to carve him into the form of a woman, embracing death as though it were life.

Outside a church, I buy *milagros*, small metal likenesses of arms, legs, hearts. The faithful pin them up behind votive candles at the church entrance, talismans endowed with prayers for the health of a sick family member. Part of me is an anthropologist, another a believer. Yet I lack the faith to use these *milagros* to grant my wish. What would such a wish entail? Nothing can be made whole.

When my week is up, the balm I'd hoped he would apply to my wounded ego hasn't healed it. I had such grand expectations for his ability to understand me, to read my soul better than anyone, that he is bound to disappoint. For a few days, he's mulled over whether to take me to the airport himself or send me by train. I lose out to an art opening in Pátzcuaro, so I'm on my own.

Fever finds me on the cold train, and I sleep fitfully. I wake in the middle of the night to a car empty save for the specter of a man on the floor beneath me, looking up my skirt. I shoo him away, but he won't move. I'm so delirious by then I'm not sure if he's real.

Behind the bed in the cheap hotel room where I stay in Mexico City the next night is a coin-operated radio. Abandoned yet again by my father. Convenient for him to imagine me more self-sufficient than I really am. A peso in the radio's slot elicits the impassioned voice of Sinéad O'Connor, singing "Nothing Compares 2 U."

13

Late-afternoon summer light dapples the trailer floor like beads of butter seeping into a warm piece of toast. At last I've reached an equilibrium: my boyfriend Robert and me in our weekend trailer home set thirty yards from my father's Catskill cabin. We've formed a strange trilogy whose easy rapport is full of fart jokes and late-night discussions on the merits of Liz Taylor's black slip in "BUtterfield 8."

Robert stirs and turns, kissing my forehead sleepily before going back under.

I wake to find it dark outside. The light above the bed blinks on and off.

Robert, dinner's ready, I whisper. My father signals us by jiggling the electric cord that supplies the trailer its juice.

Julia Child inspired my father's preparation of a roast leg of lamb appointed with fresh sprigs of rosemary—a meal that takes him hours to prepare but which is par for the course now that cooking is his passion. He bustles cheerily in the kitchen, an apron stretched over his surgically improved bosom. Since the operation, it's irksome to hug him—I don't want to encounter those too-large, projectile-like objects that don't belong on my handsome father. At least in the mountains, safe from the scrutiny of sophisticated urbanites, he ceases to whisper, forgoing the effort to mask the deep voice that fifty years of testosterone prevents from feminization. His laughter is unfettered here, too, laughter at his own corny depression-era humor:

"Mommy, Mommy! I hate daddy's guts."

"Just leave them on the side of the plate, kid. "

14

Bad day. My father blows up at the woman at the health-food store who helped me pick out herbs and dietary supplements that might reverse the cancer that has spread from his lungs to his spine. He won't eat the strawberry ice cream I churned for him nor the hamburger I've fried. He won't eat anything, in fact, and refuses to wear the size 5 Hanes Her Way underwear I bought him, correctly believing that a 5'11" man/woman needs a larger size, refusing to acknowledge that one who's shrunk from 175 to 110 pounds should wear size 5. His metabolic rate has risen, causing him to overheat constantly and strip off his clothes, even when modest guests visit. The elastic of the leg holes lies flaccid on his thighs, the too-large underwear slipping to reveal the surgically created vagina I've fought for so many years not to see.

In a tearful phone call to my mother, I bemoan his refusal to follow through with alternative therapies.

Rachel, he's dying. Let him be.

I can't. Until recently we'd still met on the tired old battleground of his refusal to introduce me as his niece. I cling to the notion that he'll finally act the part of parent instead of diva.

I rent "Smoke," a movie I think will comfort him, starring an uncharacteristically sweet Harvey Keitel. But his anxiety makes him twitchy and he keeps commenting on how depressing the movie is.

Let's go out. Let's drive.

Where, Pop? It's dark out.

Anywhere.

We prepare to leave, but then he decides against it. Nothing can calm him.

I kiss him goodnight and take the path down the dark driveway and across a patch of moss to my bed in the trailer.

Once there, I weep for the untouched meals and for my father's shrinking form—a form that has betrayed me more than once. As my tears wane, I see through the window facing the cabin a light sweeping back and forth approaching the trailer. A loud knock on the aluminum storm door, and he enters.

Standing in the doorway, emaciated, with a look of concern on his face that I can't remember having seen for months, he hands me a flashlight.

Take this. I don't want you to be frightened in the dark.

15

I'm driving up a mountain road in the Catskills. It's one of those clear days after an ice storm in which the sun creates rainbows in league with the ice-coated edges of trees, houses, fences.

The night before, I slept with a man I shouldn't have. We drank too much and had a wild time carousing in a local bar, making out on a pool table and falling into the bed he sometimes shares with his wife. I'm hung over but so clear, so clearly feeling the bittersweet pleasure of this day. This man will never be mine and that dissonance inspires me, is married to the day's transient beauty. I'm listening to one of the cassettes my father made to preserve his vinyl records. He's left hundreds of them.

Today it's "Abbey Road," a Beatles album that becomes my favorite from this moment forward. When the car reaches the top of the moun- tain, the giant, twinkling blue reservoir appears below. "I Want You (She's So Heavy)" is playing, and amid the crackle and hiss of the vinyl, I feel that my father is in the car with me, and wonder if I'll hear him cough. I realize that's impossible, that this feeling of proximity is just an illusion. Then the needle hits a rut and jumps back so that John repeats *I want you so bad,* over and over. A smile spreads across my face and the hair on the back of my neck stands up. After a minute, the needle scrapes across the record as my father's hand pushes it forward. ◆

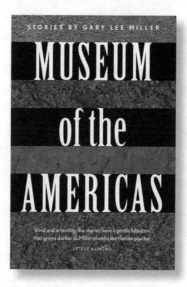

Sandra Simonds

A CAR

took me to my labor. Of
    course a car. I mean I took a car
to my day job. I took it slow.
    At some point in history, an apprentice was crying
on the knee of his master.
    Someone in South Georgia by
    the side of the road is selling
a handmade canoe. (Thought I'd never hear
from you.) A kangaroo was the evolutionary
    choice marsupial. It is
a bead. I work on it.
I polish the edges
    of my bead.
It grows on me.

Courtney Mandryk

THE LOOPED PAUSES

Hissing of the baby monitor which means he is either asleep
    or not breathing.

The hissing of the box fan, which is supposed to remind him
    of my insides.

I wish I could watch his infrared chest rise and fall.

Small blankets surround him like water on every side,
    one polka-dot one white one stripe one flowers.

When I see a leaf-clump on the road I think it is a dead cat first.

Radio on: a pile of horses mute mid-kick.

Our arugula a dead leaf pile on my plate. Or placed here
    and here to mark this:

Lapping sounds, life. The dog pivots her ears, wags her tail
    backwards.

The ice cube hits the floor.

I could gallop out to my mailbox and then gallop back. Stay.

I can't see the cats' hearts. A collage overcrowded, dog fur
    and a garden on top.

The dog sleeps, unwanting sleep, her eyes yolks, lids, yolks, lids.

I am slightly mapping, to get here and here to circumvent this:
    live sex on my plate.

I am sorry about your horses and there's nothing I can do.

A leaf on the dog's back, then another, then one in her mouth.

The dog collapses. My heart kicks.

It was not a cry just now it was the garbage truck, wet brakes
    sobbing again at the stop sign.

Rebecca Bernard

OPENINGS

June isn't sure how to stop the squirrels from getting into her apartment. She wants fresh air. The windows are wide and square. They came screenless and she can't figure out who is responsible for supplying her with new screens. The landlord is a post-office box somewhere in nearby Denton, and she was never informed of the existence of any super. The squirrels are loud during the day and louder still at night. Her phone rings. The sounds blend.

If she opens her windows and the room slowly fills with squirrels, how long will it take to get bitten? This is something June dwells on as she brews coffee and heats cans of tomato soup. Will the squirrels flood like a torrent or will it be a gentle bath of tails and fur?

June is starting to wonder if moving makes a difference. The skin of her hands and knees is hers. She has not been able to leave it behind. Now, in the Texas sun, it tightens.

◆

"I think you're in that phase where you don't answer your phone, yes?"

June listens to Rose's voice, warm over the wires.

"I'm sorry. I haven't been home much."

"Right."

When June is not working her new secretarial job, she has found that the only thing she wants to do is lie on her floor and stare at the ceiling. There is a water stain that resembles Jesus when the light hits it just so. His smile is kind.

"What time do you land on Sunday?"

"I think I get in around three or so. Then it's an hour drive to Moaning Cavern."

June wonders how many people can fit in the mind of a person. A Rose can fit in the mind of a June. But what about a hundred people? Ten? Two by two? "Great. I'll call you when I get off the plane."

A few minutes later, the line is dead and June is standing by the refrigerator. She's not hungry but she takes a leftover slice of pizza and bites into it and sits down on the kitchen floor. The grease has congealed. It's thick in her mouth.

A pain rises in her lower abdomen but she ignores it. Pain is something we leave behind, June believes. Pain does not feed. Its teeth are dulled by its nature.

◆

June's father died in a cave when she was twelve. His bones shattered by rock. Either he slipped and it was an accident or it wasn't.

The kids in middle school used to make jokes.

"If your dad dies underground and no one is around to hear it, does he make a sound?"

June heard the sound. It was blood-curdling shrieks some nights. Others, it was like a slow chant. All the things he would have said to her if he hadn't left his family to research sightless animals inside the earth.

You're a good kid. I love you. One day, Junie, you'll become someone great.

Did the blind newts lick his carcass clean before the rescue squad could find his bones?

At least her mother took the news in stride. "We are not made of soft things, June. We are rocks that God and time wear down."

◆

A knock at the door. June puts down the pizza and tenses her jaw. She gets up to open it. A short man with a mustache and wearing a tan uniform stands before her.

"I have a package for you, ma'am. Looks like they tried to deliver it somewhere in Maine first."

June nods and signs the paper. She can feel her ears wiggle slightly. The oldest nervous habit she retains from childhood.

"Thanks."

The package is large. The size of an adult greyhound. "Where would you like it to go?"

The apartment is mostly empty. A large room whose only furniture consists of a king-size bed, a tall, skinny lamp, and a handful of plants.

"Oh. Anywhere is fine." June smiles and licks her lips. Junes are meant to be blond women with thick heads of hair and plump, ready smiles. At this moment she is not a June. She feels like a Jane living inside a June costume.

The deliveryman uses his handcart to wheel the package into her apartment. June is silent. She can't think of anything to say. When he is finished, he leaves, and she is once again alone.

But she is not alone. From the corner of her eye, she sees a squirrel dart past.

June will not open the box that has arrived, because she knows what is inside, and it is a mistake. Her mother sent the bassinet before it turned out June would not be needing its services. If there is one thing June has learned, it is that only those things that are useful are worth one's time. Every June is finite. She holds her hand up to the light from the window to see the prints on her fingertips. The thin lines spiral.

◆

In late winter of her senior year of high school, June spent many afternoons outside. On the hill, by her house, she liked to watch the melting snow. Small rivulets cut through the whiteness. The earth below, revealed.

The animals her father had studied were smooth, blind creatures. They moved seamlessly in the dark. You could be near them and not even know they were there. He would tell June stories about them to help her fall asleep.

As she would stand watching the snow, she would imagine the incarnations of her younger selves sitting heavy inside of her, like Russian dolls. The heat from the sun made rivers in the snowbanks. It carved valleys that reached the mossy earth below. June asked her mother when she got home one afternoon if a person could pull out their memories—string them like prayer flags along a fence. Her mother said no. She told June to stop wasting time already. A self was too easy to let idle.

◆

"A cave is a dark place," Rose says and laughs and says it again. This time for the sensation of the echo. The cavern is nearly pitch black.

"Turn on your headlamp. You're giving me the creeps."

June and Rose are one hundred feet beneath the earth's surface and sinking deeper by the hour. Each year since they met, during their freshman year of college, Rose and June have organized an annual overnight spelunking trip.

"I can't find the switch. It's too dark."

"Here." June fumbles with Rose's headlamp. A moment later, a yellow glow emanates from above her friend's face.

"Thanks." Rose points her head forward into the darkness, exposing a thin tunnel. "How much further are we going?"

"According to the map, it looks like we got about another half mile or so before the campsite."

"It gets narrow up ahead."

June nods. She takes off a glove to feel the side of the cave wall with her bare finger. The oil leaves an imprint. An oval.

Rose has started moving and June regloves her hand to follow along. She can feel the heat from their bodies collecting. It mingles with the cool, damp earth, but nothing is left behind.

◆

Her father flew her in a plane when she was ten. From high above, the United States looked like a tapestry. Trees, farms, barns, skyscrapers, junked cars, drainage ditches, power lines stretching their arms like seams along a massive quilt.

June wanted to know it all. To touch all doors and see all shoots of grass. Everything that existed was unique. She closed her eyes and imagined the hearts of all things living, beating. The sound didn't stop. It couldn't. It was the loudest thing, and June joined the rhythm. There was so much to know and so much to forget.

◆

Crawling through the cave, June's mind is visited by thoughts of her new home. Hardwood floors. A box. Squirrel tails. Windows.

She had not yet plugged in her television, but the first week in the apartment she found herself watching the blank screen. It seemed full of possibility. She wondered what might be on. Whose face she might be missing.

Reflections of the squirrels would pass by every so often, but she could blink them away. Were their faces reflecting off the dark glass now?

Is the box shifting alone in the empty apartment? Is that possible?

Rose looks at her. "You alright, J?"

◆

An hour later, they have stopped to eat lunch in a midsize cavern. Stalagmites grow on the floor to their right. Rose takes a sip of water and sighs. The exhalation booms off the ceiling. "I'm glad to see you, you know."

"Same here." June smiles, but Rose's headlamp is facing the other direction, so Rose doesn't see it.

"Did I tell you I moved? It's a bigger place in the same neighborhood. It's got a porch—I like that. An extra bedroom for George's office and all."

"That sounds really nice."

Rose fumbles with her sandwich wrapper. The plastic ruffling makes the quiet quieter.

"My new place has a lot of squirrels."

"What?" Rose turns to look at June. The glow of their headlamps forms an arc.

"My new apartment. There are a lot of squirrels living outside. They're all over—on the ledges, the windows, trees out front."

"Is that a problem?"

June chews the last bite of her sandwich and watches as Rose takes a sip of water from a bottle. "I don't know."

◆

June has lived in eight cities in the six years since she graduated from college. In most cities, she has worked in an office. She is transferable and easy, good at finding what she wants.

In Gainesville, it was Marcus. In Erie, it was Palmer. In Rockland, it was a man whose name she cannot remember. In Eureka, it was Nick and Tyler and Ben. In Stamford, it was Alan, but it felt like no one.

The men June sleeps with do not define her life. Sometimes she barely knows them. Love need not surface to make a place a place. Yet there is memory embedded in hand-holding. And where there is memory, there is something worth leaving. They are ice cubes and June is the ice-cube tray. She holds the faces and moments and indentations in her head until they are frozen over, and then pop. They melt in the hot sun as she drives onward. The moment was had, held and now gone. She is ready for the next best thing.

◆

June pictures the box waiting in her apartment in Texas. The bassinet inside is beginning to clear its throat. Slowly settling cardboard shifting in the night. The squirrels can hear it from outside the glass windows.

She imagines the squirrels have voices. They speak to the box. I know what's inside of you. Tick tick. My claws could tear you open. I will chew through your tape. Let me near. Show me the way. I have never felt more hungry.

Who has abandoned you? Why has she done this?

◆

June's father had been a tall man. When she was small, she sat on his shoulders so she could look down upon the earth. His arms, like branches, cradled her.

But the early memories are more and more difficult to pick apart. She was sitting in the back yard and he was nearby. A shadow cast on the green grass.

Was she playing with something? A tennis ball, a stick? She knows that memories are like rivulets through the brain, carving the same path again and again. Each time slightly different.

He was laughing and pointing up at the sky, but there weren't any stars, because it was daylight. So why was he doing it?

He was pointing up at the sun, and it was blinding her. And he was saying, Look Junie, look, all that light, from all those stars, and most of them are already gone. And why did he say that to her?

But did this happen or did she make it up or did her mother tell her about it once he was gone?

◆

The first time one move bled into the next was in Baltimore. Greg had tracked June down.

Greg. A name she felt was always caught in the back of her throat. Like gargling. Greg. Geg. Gleg. But he had been different from the others, something there. Something that could be ruined. Almost an entire year had passed since their affair. Since she left him without notice.

Knock knock.

She was wearing a men's button-down shirt over a sports bra. Her hair was up in a ponytail, mascara caked on from the night before.

She answered.

Greg stepped forward before she could recoil, and then she was in his arms. His spindly arms like some birch tree strangling her. He was trying to talk but he wasn't saying any words.

June didn't know what to say either. She watched the reflection of the back of Greg's head in the mirror.

Greg was crying, but he was also smiling. His fingers tightened around her back. He was hurting her—did he know it?

"I'm sorry," she said. She took a step backward and sat on the unmade futon in her living room. He followed. June put a hand up to the place where the skin covered her heart. Greg's mouth looked toothy. Like excess bone was about to fall out in his eagerness to make her care.

Greg came close to her again and his bony legs brushed against her knees. He leaned down to put his arms on her shoulders and his body formed a cage around her own.

She tried to stand up, and, to her surprise, he let her. If he really wanted to keep her, he shouldn't have let her out.

The front door was still open and she could see the fluorescent light coming in from the hallway. There was a symphony in her ears. The sound of lowing cellos. His smell was so familiar.

"You really shouldn't be here. I'm sorry." June sounded weak, even to herself.

He didn't look sad when he looked at her. It was confusion. He was sitting on the futon, his fingers running over a corner of the sheet. She watched as his hands slowly stopped moving. His eyes looked over the room, seeing her small life. The cheap furniture and clothes on the floor. Then he spoke: "Why are you living here?"

June looked around the room, at the view from her window of a brick wall. She started, slowly, to unbutton her shirt.

Greg left later that night and June considered how odd it was to watch him go. She hated how paper-like he looked as he stood in her doorway. Something to be torn and shredded. But he could have said the same thing about her.

◆

"Do you think you'll end up moving again?" Rose heats coffee over a small portable stove in a large vacuous cavern. The cool air currents of the underground diffuse the small waves of heat released.

It smells like burning. June sits cross-legged using her gloved finger to trace shapes in the dusty surface of the ground. Her stomach begins to cramp.

Rose continues, "I just wonder if you'll ever settle down is all."

"You think you and George'll get married?" June smooths away the rectangle she has drawn.

Rose pours the coffee into two cups and passes one to June. "Probably. I don't know when. But one of these years."

June lies back and bites her tongue. She shines her flashlight beam along the ceiling, looking for images of God. For a human face.

"I'd be your maid of honor—if you wanted me."

Rose is silent. June can sense something through the space between their bodies. A guilt like a slim animal between them. "I don't know if I want to keep moving around like I do."

"Then stop." Rose turns off the stove to let it cool off. "Isn't it easier to stop than to keep going?"

June pictures faces. There is something painful about being held by someone who will never hold you again—but it is also good. They are her memories—she owns them. It is too hard to explain. It is the box that has interfered. This new memory to cloud the others. "It's real good to see you, you know."

Rose swings her beam of light like a pendulum toward June. "Of course, J. It always is."

◆

When did she start to confuse places? In Baltimore? Before? June would think about going to the grocery store and not remember which state she was living in. With her eyes closed she would picture sleeping next to someone, and not remember the individual features.

Each bedroom she lived in had walls like a cavern. Either white or taupe or cream. They echoed one another, and when she would wake up she could imagine herself anywhere. When she was being touched, she owned the moment. It was a one-night stand but it was *her* one-night stand. The memories whorl in her mind.

He died in a cave, but he returned to her dreams. She could have held the baby's hands, but it died before they formed. So it wasn't really a baby. And they weren't really hands.

It was for the best. One life shouldn't bleed into the next. She can't even open her own windows.

When she thinks about the places in which she has lived, they start to look less and less distinct. Sometimes she has to shut her eyes so it stops happening. There should only be right now.

When she passes by other Junes on the streets in her dreams, this is what is happening. She wanted to live like this. It was her choice. But did she realize how many bodies would fill her mind? How many memories were hard to leave behind?

◆

"If I decided to stay where I'm living now—how would I do that?" June says this to Rose's back as they walk through the final passageway which leads to their campsite for the night.

"What do you mean?" Rose sets down her pack and turns to look at June.

There is a thin shaft of light coming down from high above their heads. A crack in the earth's skin far above. June shrugs. "How do I know it's the right place to be?"

"Is there such a thing?"

"I figured you would know, if anyone."

Rose kneels down and begins to unroll her sleeping bag. "Well, what's been not right with every place so far?"

June closes her eyes and tries to see the different cities. Her different selves. She doesn't want to picture them right now. She can't. "Do you ever think about having kids?"

"Yes. Sometimes. I think I'd like to." Rose smiles. "Do you ever?"

June sits down and puts a hand up to her face, feeling her jaw. "No. I mean, I'm not sure I will again."

Rose looks at June, her headlamp striking June's left cheek. June frowns. "I swear it's an infestation. Bushy tails everywhere you look."

◆

June had left Baltimore soon after Greg's visit. She didn't feel ready to leave but needed to find a new place, something untouched by other places, other people, her other lives.

She had sometimes wondered what would happen if she became pregnant. In Maine, she found out. Greg was following her still, but this time he didn't know it.

The only person she told was her mother, so when the loss happened it was okay. There were no terrible phone calls to be made. She blamed herself alone. Look, now once again, she was free. Her mother always told her to settle her pain on her own. But did any of the Junes inside of her know what they should be feeling?

The move to Texas was not joyful. The delayed package from her mother followed her. But no one else did and no one else would.

◆

In her dream that night, June returns from the grocery store with a sack of eggs and flour and almonds. The box in her living room looks nearly twice its original size. But she knows this isn't possible.

She places the nuts on the windowsill in the kitchen in plain sight of the squirrels. Her plan is to lure them away from the bedroom. She is tired of their nightly conversations and murmurings. It is too much. It is as if God has descended into her apartment and does not want her to sleep.

You've had one too many lives, Jane.

My name isn't Jane, it's June.

I know who you are.

Do you really?

Of course. And I love you very much.

June wakes up and turns to Rose, but Rose is asleep and peaceful. It is not fair to wake her.

Before she left to meet Rose for this trip, she went by the Home Depot to look for replacement screens, but they had nothing that would fit. She isn't sure how she would go about installing them on her own anyhow. She doesn't want to get bitten while she tries, while the glass is partially raised. She doesn't own a ladder.

June pictures the squirrels. They have tiny brains but sharp teeth. From up close their tails are not lovely but flecked with insects and dirt.

She wishes that the squirrels sounded less like God and more like her father. He would tell her about the earth. Water runs down hills and forms oceans. Oceans have volcanoes underground. Magma can pop out of the earth's surface underwater—it's that hot. Something can open up and stay so hot that magma flows, even underwater.

Why did she let Gleg go?

Where do all the memories run to? Where do they live?

◆

They were in the kitchen and she was four years old. It is maybe the earliest memory that June claims to possess, and sometimes she hates that she has remembered anything at all. It is fat with use. She doesn't remember the event itself anymore. She can only see the memory of the event—the path her brain has rubbed raw.

Each time it comes to her, it tells her she cannot be a new June, unconnected from the old. He is with her in all worlds. All of her memories exist in all her worlds. It is what makes her hands feel like her hands, even when she is asleep. She is a person, like any other.

In the memory, water is running. He stands near her, but she cannot smell him, her father. They wash red paint out of their hands. It rivulets through their fingers, the creases. It happens over and over. They are both smiling. She doesn't know then that one day all things will be gone.

◆

In the cave the next morning, Rose is quieter than normal. June wants to clear the air but isn't sure what to say. They heat coffee and eat granola bars and then begin to pack for their departure.

As they begin their ascent through the cave, June thinks about telling Rose that maybe they have moved past the point of caving. That maybe this way of coming together has run its course.

"I always forget how excited I am to see daylight by the end of these trips." Rose is leading the way, and her words drift backwards to June's ears.

"It'll be nice to get back to real life," June says.

The night before, as they were falling asleep, Rose had asked her if she spent a lot of time alone in her day-to-day life. If that was how she liked it. The question threw June off. She told Rose that yes, she was quite used to being alone. But somehow the answer didn't seem right. Had growing something inside made her change her mind about being alone? Briefly, being so close to something else?

Rose said the reason she asked was because of something June had told her once. "You remember telling me about this guy named...Greg, I think it was. You said that when you slept with him you would look over his shoulder and stare at the wall, and think about all the people who had looked at that wall. It always seemed like the saddest thing to think. I mean, why would you think about a wall when you're that close to another human being?"

That night, she told Rose it was just about the experience. Her life was a collection of experiences, like everyone else's, but hers were just more varied. It was nice to be a part of many worlds, many lives.

Rose turns to look back at June. "How much longer, you think? I feel like I can already see the beginnings of natural light."

"Yeah, it's strange how deep it penetrates. I think we've still got another half mile."

They crawl on in silence. For how many years has June forced Rose to crawl below the surface of the earth? To search in darkness for a ghost. An unreal thing.

"June?" Rose has stopped because June has stopped.

June looks up and the beam of her headlamp meets the beam of Rose's lamp. She reaches up and turns off her light. "I think I can see the glow of the sun up ahead."

"Thank God."

◆

The box moans. The squirrels pile one atop the other. Although she knows it sounds immature, June has always told herself it is the ones she barely knows that she loves the most. Every touch is infinite when it continues in her mind. In this world, she knew her father for a thousand years. In this world, he loved her always. In this world, he had hands the size of walruses. In this world, he never died.

◆

When they reach the entrance to the cave, they are bathed in sunlight. It is blinding but not unkind. June feels a kind of joy at the center of her stomach. It is the feeling she gets when she starts a new life—she cannot see anything and yet she knows she is alive. She glances at Rose's face and wonders what she is thinking.

◆

Two weeks after the trip to Moaning Cavern, Rose calls and leaves a message on her machine. June saves it so she can hear it again. "I just heard from your mother. I'm sorry. Why didn't you tell me?"

June has not yet returned the call.

Sometimes the squirrels butt their heads against the windows by the dish of almonds she has placed on the sill, and it makes her feel cruel. She should sprinkle some of them outside. But then perhaps they will become reliant. She is worried that if she doesn't figure something out soon they will find a way to get inside. Whether or not the windows are open. Whether or not they have screens. She imagines they form pyramids at night. Their happy teeth. Their voices, like God. Like her father. Each one sings a memory she has already heard before.

It is her fault. There is impermanence in her being. The blood ticks inside her veins. This memory will rub her mind raw.

June stands and walks toward the window. On the ledge, a squirrel on its hind legs peers in. ◆

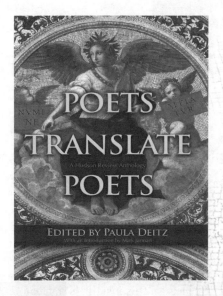

Han Dong

THE RED FLAG FALLS

(translated by Nicky Harman)

The red flag floats from the building's roof
A red flag falling is a terrible sight.

I understand the red flag, but not the birds in the sky
I understand armed struggle, but not nature in flux.

I understand my mother
Her fear, at this instant, is my fear.

At the entrance gate, my mother stops the bike
And my foot gets stuck between the spokes.

But there's no pain, because
Look, the red flag's floating from the rooftop.

As if someone has been pushed out of the window
Spurting a brilliant red before touching earth

It is too clear an insight for a child.
The red flag

Tilts slowly, falls, furling, unfolding
Skimming every window, closed and open, of the building.

Karen Stefano

UNDONE

The doctor asks if I'll agree to take some tests. Simple stuff—reflex, Rorschach, Minnesota Multiphasic Personality Inventory. I don't see the harm, so I say yes. But I start having second thoughts.

The State of California can lock you up for seventy-two hours if you're a danger to yourself. I hit hour fifty-one before I remember the state can also commit you to a mental hospital for a whole year. A judge decides this after a 3.2-minute hearing, so you can bet that judge stakes a lot on the intake doctor's report, a doctor who in my case keeps asking, "How does someone like you wind up here?" until I want to slap him.

I know I messed up pretty badly. I understand that now, but I'm fairly certain a year in here will only make things worse. And considering this past year and beyond, the things that led me here, I'm not so sure my life can be inventoried.

I open the test booklet anyway. If I have to, I'll use their tool. I'll play along and use their words to tell my story. They want a map to crazy? I'll show them crazy. I'll show them just how easily it all comes undone.

THIS PERSONALITY INVENTORY consists of random statements. Read each statement and decide whether it is true or false as applied to you. If a statement is true, blacken the bubble marked T on the sheet provided. If a statement is false, blacken the circle marked F. *Use only a No. 2 pencil.* A separate sheet is provided in the event you feel compelled to explain your answers.

1. *I am friendly, even toward people doing things considered wrong. (True)*

Last January, barely two years out of law school, I got promoted to felonies. No more misdemeanor domestic violence, petty theft, or traffic court. Now I represented rapists, drug dealers, child molesters, men who fucked their wives up good. I was on the way up.

"The whole point of being a lawyer is to handle bigger and better cases," my boss Henry said, giving me the news. In the L.A. Public

Defender's Office, "bigger and better" meant clients facing decades in prison, maybe a third strike, and facts that curled your hair. My new stack of files included a vehicular manslaughter, possession for sale of twenty kilos of cocaine, and rape of an eighty-year-old woman at gunpoint. They were slated for trial one after the other.

I was in way over my head, but I loved Henry's attitude and crowded around to hear his stories at the bar, where a party had been thrown together in my honor. Any defense lawyer was sick of getting cornered at parties and tortured with questions like, "How can you defend those people?" But unlike me, Henry had all the answers.

"My uncle once asked, 'How would you feel if you set a guilty man free with your fast talking?'" Henry swigged his beer, pausing before feeding his punch line. "I'd feel great! Putting a guilty man back on the street is the greatest testament to my skills as a trial lawyer."

We cheered and raised our glasses, but even though it was my big night, my laughter was forced. Pumped up on beers and bravado, it was all about ego, who was the best, who got away with something in court. Lawyers were like a pack of dogs who took comfort in one another. Together we were strong; alone, weak. At home, in the darkness before sleep, we would all feel differently.

I snuck outside to call my Dad and tell him about my promotion.

"Honey, that's wonderful," he said. "I'm so proud of you."

If my father had reservations about his only child's career choice, he kept them to himself. He might not always understand me, but his devotion had proven life's only certainty.

"How are you feeling?" I asked.

"I'm in pretty good shape." He coughed. "For the shape I'm in."

"I'll see you for dinner Sunday?"

"Sure thing, honey."

I hung up and returned to the pack for one more round.

2. When I feel sad, talking to a friend cheers me up. (True)

When Evelyn worked at the Public Defender's office, we walked nightly to the jail to see whatever clients we couldn't counsel in the tank at court. Afterwards, we slumped into Jonny-O's to drink off the day and lard ourselves with Happy Hour food. We commiserated and, when one of us was in trial, tried out our opening statements. When Jonny broke down the buffet, it was time to finish our vodkas and head home. It felt good to have someone to talk to, someone who made me less scared. The pace and stakes of felonies had staggered me and I no longer drank to take the edge off. I drank to get numb.

A month after my promotion, Evelyn informed me in a guilty voice that she had accepted a job with a corporate-litigation firm. She was drowning in student loans, sick of squeaking by on the shit salary they paid us at the P.D.'s office. We'd still see each other all the time, she promised.

"It's cool," I said. I bought her drinks to show what a good friend I was, that I wasn't worried at all about how I would survive in the cesspool without her.

3. Love has disappointed me. (True)

The first time we slept together, Frank bit my nipples until they bled, his thin white lips persisting despite my polite attempts to wriggle out of range. When he rammed inside me, I felt no pleasure except the relief in not being alone. He said things during sex like, "Nowhere to run, huh baby?" and "Filthy whore." It startled me at first, then I noticed I liked it. After a sissified groan, Frank pulled out of me, rolled over and launched into a peroration on himself. I had an awful feeling he might expect me to talk about myself, but he just wanted someone to hear his words. I realized I didn't want to listen. I had my own problems.

Frank had alcohol issues. Not an addiction like I had developed, but a problem. Whenever he drank he became a real asshole. On St. Patrick's Day, after too many green beers, we cut down an alley behind Jonny-O's, staggering back to my rented one-bedroom craftsman. Frank was ranting about the lawyers in his courtroom who had walked all over him and shown him no respect. I said he shouldn't take it personally, they were just standing up for their clients. That's when the back of his hand flew backwards and cracked me across the bridge of my nose, knocking me on my ass. I stayed put for a minute, trying to figure out what just happened. Frank kept walking.

The next morning the phone rang as I stared into the mirror, admiring my shiner and fingering the fragile azure skin around my eye.

"Hey," Frank said when I picked up. His voice sounded mopey and contrite, a puppy who pissed on the rug. "Sorry about what happened."

I didn't know what I was supposed to say.

"I was fucked up and . . ." Frank paused, waiting for me to speak.

I sat there, soaking up the silence.

"Listen, Janet. You're not going to tell anyone, are you?"

Frank was a Superior Court judge who heard criminal cases. He had served as a panelist on "The Ravages of Crystal Methamphetamine on the Criminal Justice System" at the Spring Symposium of the Los Angeles Trial Lawyers Association. Afterwards, Frank lingered over his martini, we got to talking, and he ended up coming home with me. Frank had a reputation for meting out stern lectures and maximum jail time to any domestic-violence offender sentenced in his court.

I didn't speak, didn't hang up, and didn't stop seeing him.

The next time it happened, we were camping deep in the Santa Ynez Mountains. Frank hadn't been drinking, he was just in a really bad mood. He shattered my right cheekbone and left me on the side of Highway 33 with my thumb in the air.

After that it became easy to avoid him. The presiding judge had quit assigning my cases to Frank when it became public knowledge we were sleeping together. I stopped going out, so I only had to worry about chance meetings in the echoing corridors of the Hall of Justice.

There weren't any.

4. I have problems with authority. (True)

"Counsel, approach the bench."

I stepped across the courtroom with Luke Banderman, wondering what this was about. Judge Nelson was a grouchy bastard and former D.A. who made no effort to conceal his loathing of defense attorneys and the scum we represented. Nelson had lost use of his right leg after being shot in a hunting accident and for the past ten years presided from the bench in a wheelchair. Lawyers in my office called him "Ironside" behind his back.

Luke wore charcoal Prada, accented with a striped silk tie. Court TV had picked up Luke's last murder trial and female viewers phoned in record numbers to inquire about his marital status. Luke spent every penny on his wardrobe, always prepared to reward his local fan base if Eyewitness 5 stopped by for his opinion on that week's high profile homicide. Jurors and judges ate him up, but his Eddie Haskell demeanor stabbed beneath my skin.

"How much longer with this witness?" whispered Ironside when we reached the bench.

"Ten minutes," I said.

"Good. I have an appointment I need to get to. I understand this will finish the prosecution's case and the defense can call its first witness after lunch."

After I finished cross-examination, Ironside straightened up in his chair and flashed a row of brown teeth at the jury. "Ladies and Gentlemen, now seems like a propitious time for our lunch recess. You are excused until one-thirty."

I motioned for my client, Carl Williams, to stand while the judge rolled down from the bench. Carl leaned in and whispered, "Does that mean we get to eat now? Or we don't get to eat?"

"Sshhh." I smiled at the jury as they filed out.

The bad news was that my client had hit a guy with his car in broad daylight while speeding and the guy had died. The good news was that Carl had only been going 42 in a 35 zone and had not been drunk or high. The D.A.'s office didn't care and charged my client with vehicular manslaughter, despite his clean record, steady janitorial job, and wife and infant son. Luke Banderman wanted Carl in prison.

The really good news was that my investigation had revealed that the dead guy had been jaywalking, after stepping out of a bar at 2:00 P.M. on a Tuesday, a bar he frequented daily. The bartender, Les Weidl, recalled the alleged victim had consumed his usual afternoon trifecta of a beer and two bourbons. The really, really good news—as good as it got in my line of work—was that the dead guy had had eye surgery the day before the accident, a surgery that, according to his own doctor, could have impacted his vision and orientation when stepping out of a dark bar into the blinding afternoon sunshine. With this evidence, no jury in the world would convict Carl.

I was going to mop the floor with Luke Banderman.

5. Sometimes I feel nothing ever goes right for me. (True)

I scrambled to my office. I had sixty minutes to meet with my doctor and bartender witnesses—neither of whom were thrilled to testify—finalize my direct examination, scarf down some food, race back to meet Carl and answer his inevitable questions, and be ready to go at one-thirty on the dot or risk getting chewed out by Ironside in front of the jury.

I stared in disbelief at the empty conference room.

"Where's Mr. Weidl and Dr. Spradley?" I asked the receptionist.

"Who?"

"Weidl! Spradley! My witnesses! Where are they?"

"Janet, nobody's checked in for you."

I tried to calm myself, hoping they had gone directly to court. I riffled through my file to see where I ordered them to appear. A jolt of panic hit as I found the subpoenas, in triplicate, in the back of the file. My secretary had prepared the subpoenas, but I had stuffed them in the file and forgotten to have them served. Without proper service, neither witness had any obligation to testify, and neither would do it voluntarily.

Each had made that abundantly clear. Without their testimony, Carl was doomed.

"Fuck!" I screamed and ran to find help, but the office was deserted. I called the bar, but Weidl had gone fishing. I called the surgeon, but he was in surgery. Two star witnesses unreachable because I had failed to subpoena them. This was a fuck-up of epic proportions.

6. Sometimes I want to smash things. (True)

Your Honor, the defense seeks a recess until tomorrow afternoon." In a chambers conference, I confessed to Luke and Ironside what had happened, detailing the exculpatory testimony these witnesses would give. I told them about the subpoenas. I told them it was all my fault.

"Your Honor, we object to a continuance of any length," Luke said.

Ironside shook his head. "There will be no continuance, counsel."

"But Your Honor, without this testimony my innocent client is certain to be convicted. My failure to subpoena these witnesses will constitute grounds for a reversal of the conviction due to ineffective assistance of counsel—"

"Not my problem, counsel. Call a witness or we move to closing statements."

I argued. I fought. I made a complete record of my incompetence. Back inside the courtroom, Carl slouched in his borrowed suit. Ironside had allowed me five minutes to explain to my client how he would now go to prison because of my fuck-up. Carl would likely only serve half the sentence before it got reversed on appeal. As Carl absorbed the news, I glanced around the courtroom at the bailiff, Ironside's clerk, Luke. The Hall of Justice henchmen loved gossip and news of my monumental screwup would spread like wildfire. I tried to enjoy the final moments of having been a semi-respected trial lawyer.

With no witnesses to call, we launched into closing arguments. The jury came back with a guilty verdict forty minutes later. At the office, I confessed to Henry, who grimaced and dialed the county's malpractice-insurance carrier.

I was having a bad year. In addition to my committing malpractice and torpedoing my career, my father had started spitting up blood again, something that's not technically supposed to happen to someone in remission. He went to the doctor and confirmed what I already knew. The cancer had returned. This time, with a vengeance.

7. I try to act polite, even when others are critical. (True)

Driving home from work, my head throbbed. I was out of vodka and had no choice but to stop and refuel.

The Safeway parking lot swarmed with cars and as I turned down a packed aisle, I realized I was heading the wrong direction. "Shit," I whispered under my breath.

Another car started up the row, driving the proper direction, and a twinge of guilt prickled my skin. The asshole in this scenario was me and I hated being the asshole. I had been the asshole all day, as Carl Williams would certainly agree.

I spied an open parking place. As I steered hard to maneuver into the awkward angle, the car from the end of the aisle gunned it, braking with a screech an inch from my bumper.

"That was my spot, you fucking bitch!" the driver screamed.

Even in the falling darkness, I could see blackheads riddling her flattened nose. Gray-streaked hair hung from under a Minnie Pearl hat and I couldn't help looking for a dangling price tag. "Sorry." I heard my voice sound sheepish. I'd felt sorry all day. No, all year. When would I stop feeling sorry for everything?

A car behind Minnie Pearl honked and she responded with a stiff and defiant middle finger.

"You fucking cunt!" she shrieked at me again. Her venom pierced my skin and soaked through to my spinal cord. She lurched into another space, climbed out of her car, and hovered near it. She was still yelling, but I couldn't make out the words. Finally she ambled toward the market entrance, and the glass doors and bright lights swallowed her up. As I started to step out of my car, I realized I hadn't turned off the engine or unfastened my seat belt. I sat for a minute and watched my hands tremble on the wheel.

At home I drank my Stoli, playing the confrontation over in my head, weighing the Dalai Lama retort against the Sonny Corleone. But really, it wasn't my fault, I wanted to say. It was an innocent mistake. I'm a good person. People used to like me.

I took a Vicodin, left over from Frank, and started to feel better.

8. I have a healthy appetite. (False)

I stared at my reflection in the refrigerator door. We had a four-day Fourth of July weekend and I had spent mine on the couch, watching "Gilligan's Island." I hadn't showered in three days and a stain bled across my sweatshirt where yesterday's coffee had managed to miss my mouth.

After ruining Carl's life and my reputation, and what with everything else, it had gotten hard to get out of bed. I started biting my nails, stopped showing up at parties, drank at home instead of at Jonny-O's. Evelyn left messages I didn't return, and eventually she stopped calling.

I opened the refrigerator and peered inside. The slick white sides were still spotless after the scouring they received during a brief, misguided bout with sobriety. The shelves held a shriveled plum and four cans of Coors.

Someone told me that my father dropped a beer can on my head when I was three. He was rummaging the fridge for the minced ham, unaware I had pattered after him into the kitchen. I had no recollection of this and didn't know if it was true, though my father was a clumsy man and I did have an odd dent in my skull. I closed the door and poured all four Coors down my throat, wondering. Did I drink because my life was fucked up? Or was my life fucked up because I drank?

9. Evil spirits possess me. (True)

I had just turned ten in 1974 when Hollywood unleashed "The Exorcist." Despite my parents' sheltering, I had still learned the movie contained images so disturbing that theatres provided "Exorcist barf bags," patrons fainted during screenings, and a San Francisco woman committed suicide after watching it. Theatres across the country hired security guards to ward off the twin evils of hysteria and six-figure liability.

Four weeks earlier, my mother had packed up and left, leaving not so much as a note, and my father was desperate to maintain some semblance of normalcy in my life. This meant a lot of things to my father but on a windy March Saturday, it meant spending his day off standing watch outside Food Basket, where I peddled candy with six other Camp Fire Girls.

Food Basket stood next to the Pacific Theatre, where "The Exorcist" was playing. Between customers, I watched my father slit his eyes in the direction of moviegoers offering tickets to a velour-clad usher. He paced between me and the other Camp Fire Girls, hands stuffed in his pockets, relaxing only when the last of the patrons disappeared into air-conditioned darkness. When my father trotted to the car for another case of Almond Rocca, I stole an opportunity to study the poster beneath the marquee. The scene of a man holding a briefcase under the shadows of a lamppost revealed nothing. But the message fueled my fears: "Nobody expected it, nobody believed it and nobody could stop it. The one hope, the only hope: THE EXORCIST."

After we closed up shop for the day, my friend Tess Thompson and I accompanied my father inside Food Basket. While Dad shopped, we made a beeline for the magazines to peruse *Teen Beat* and *Tiger Beat*, periodicals our parents refused to buy for us. Tess flipped the soft, grainy pages past photos of Donny Osmond to the Cinema section. On the page was a benign photo of a girl in a white nightgown, propped against pillows in her bed, looking expectantly at a priest. "Linda Blair in The Exorcist," read the caption. Another jolt of fear hit my chest. Tess read aloud, "When the priest enters, the room is bitter cold—a sure sign of evil."

"I don't get it," I said, my voice wavering.

Tess was a tubby, pug-nosed girl. She smelled faintly of rotting cheese, but her self-esteem dwarfed mine. "She's possessed, dummy."

"Possessed?"

"By Satan." Tess hissed the *"ssss"* and widened her eyes for effect. "And it's a true story, you know."

Tess explained with her usual authority that Satan frequently entered the bodies of girls our age, generally avoiding Catholics (Tess happened to be Catholic) and gravitating toward sinners. She pointed to a *Tiger Beat* caption listing additional signs of possession—unusual strength, and levitation.

Then Tess dropped the bomb. "The girl it happened to? You know, that the movie's about? She came from a broken family." Tess paused and leveled her eyes on me. "Just like you."

"Girls, let's go," my father called as he steered a grocery cart past us. Tess shoved *Tiger Beat* back into the rack and we ran to the parking lot.

That night, as I got ready for bed, my room felt cold.

"It's chilly in here, isn't it?" I asked when my father came to kiss me goodnight.

"Then get under the covers."

"In fact, it's bitter cold, wouldn't you say?"

"Don't be ridiculous," he huffed. "Good night." He snapped off the light and went to bed.

"Dad?" I stage-whispered.

"Go to sleep!" he yelled. My father was a patient man, but not when it came time for sleep.

I lay in the dark, heart pounding, desperate to gauge the temperature, trying to convince myself I wasn't that strong. My mind raced with visions of priests waving crosses over me, chanting in Latin, then stepping out to our kitchen to shake their heads silently at my father. I saw my face transformed into a demon's, head spinning on my neck, mouth spewing bile. Doom settled over me as I realized that not only were we not Catholic, we weren't religious at all. I had attended Missionary Christ Temple after two men holding gold-trimmed Bibles knocked on our door one Saturday. The clean-cut gentlemen offered free rides in their van to and from Sunday School, and my mother jumped at the offer. I attended for two months, until, one Sunday, while my eyes were closed in prayer, someone stole my collection-plate money from my purse. I never returned. One little setback and I had turned my back on God. Clearly, I was a sinner.

My world had turned upside down when my mother left, but now, as I lay awake in my bed, everything made sense in my ten-year-old mind. I was possessed by Satan and my mother had seen it. What would my father do when he learned why his wife had left? He could never forgive me and he would inevitably leave me too.

For months, the terror of my secret controlled me. I withdrew, spending hours at the mirror, searching for the signs of Satan my mother had seen, often finding evil in my shining eyes. Violating his principles, my father sent me to a child psychiatrist, a fat man with Dumbo-like ears who insisted that I act out dramas of abandonment with dolls. I gave him what he wanted, even confessed to a fear of the dark, but I guarded my secret. My mother had already left. I planned to hold on to my father for as long as I could.

10. *I would enjoy working as a librarian. (False)*

Carver Junior High School maintained the typical 1970s Southern California teen social hierarchy. Those groups divided first by race: Blacks, Whites, Mexicans, Vietnamese. White kids then roughly subcategorized into Dorks, Brains, Jocks, Surfers, and Stoners. I was nervous and overeager, features that ensured my Dork status. My eighth-grade year had begun miserably when I started my period without realizing it. I walked all over campus with a stain seeping across the seat of my white Dittos until Ms. McElroy, the gym teacher, pulled me into the bathroom and explained what had happened.

Halfway through the school year, a campus cop caught Danny Green and me smoking pot behind the handball courts. On my behalf, my shamed father negotiated a punishment of three days' suspension and a semester with Mr. Lazarro, Senior Librarian. Mr. Lazarro oversaw detention, an extra period tacked onto six regular class hours of the school day, for extra cash, he told us kids. Mr. Lazarro had a face like an owl and wore skintight polyester bell-bottoms and platform shoes. Under his watch every afternoon, the girls sat on one side of the room, where we flipped our feathered hair and fingered puka-shell necklaces, writing each other notes and swinging freshly shaved legs. Guys sat on the other side, drawing lightning bolts or staring off into space. My crime had proven a turning point, giving me entrée into the elite society of Stoners, a networking opportunity that would shape my teenage years.

My mother resurfaced that year, phoning after four years of silence, brimming with tearful apologies, asking if she could still be part of my life. I rode the No. 7 bus to her apartment the day after her call. Her one-room home was a dim hole. It bordered an alley emitting sounds of homeless men dumpster-diving and pulverizing each other with angry fists. I pretended it didn't depress me while my mother fed me jelly donuts and two-percent milk. She sat across from me, chain-smoking Virginia Slims, her mouth twitching smiles and peppering me with questions. Did I like school? Did I have a boyfriend? For three months I visited her every Monday, her one day off from The Chicken Pie Shop, where she waitressed for minimum wage and fifteen percent of $2.99 Early Bird specials. Then she lost weight. She quit talking when I came over. She finally told me to stop coming at all.

I broached the subject with my father that night at dinner. "Dad, can Mom come live with us? I think she needs us now."

"What's done can't be undone," my father said and sat down to eat. His quivering lip belied his stern tone.

Serving out my sentence in detention, I wondered. Did Mr. Lazarro aspire to become a junior-high librarian? Or was it just the space he landed in after a downward spiral, complete with compromises and justifications? Between breaking up occasional fights and stepping outside to sneak a smoke, Mr. Lazarro sat at his desk reading *Popular Mechanics* while we delinquents copied text from The Encyclopædia Britannica, intending to pass it off in Social Studies as carefully researched reports. Afterwards, I studied *Seventeen* magazine, straining to uncover the secrets of teen popularity. At the end of the year, we wrote sentimental words with undercurrents of truth in each other's yearbooks:

Janet, I didn't talk to you to much this year, but your a really sweet person. Elyse

Janet, Glad we became friends. Sure hope we stay that way. Joey

Janet, Watch out for the guys—they're sly devils! Love ya, Nance

On the last day of school, I felt a twinge of nostalgia saying goodbye to Mr. Lazarro, then shrugged it off as I came home to get ready for the Eighth Grade Dance. I inserted my key in the lock, but the door swung open before I could turn it and I practically fell inside the house. I looked up to see my father's ashen face. He was home early from work, something that had never happened before.

"What's wrong?" I asked.

He sat down at the kitchen table and put his face in his thick hands, muffling sobs. "Your mother killed herself," he said, his voice cracking. He had never stopped wearing his gold wedding band, and in that moment it seemed to burn on his finger.

That was the day I learned to expect the worst.

11. *After a rough day, I need a few drinks to relax. (True)*

Celebrating the last weekend of summer with a party?" asked the checkout girl.

"Yeah," I lied.

I now purchased my vodka in the economical 1.75-liter size with the handle fused into the glass. Booze was the only thing I could count on, my reward for making it through another workday of assholes whispering behind my back. Booze washed away everything, even my father's decay, a decay that had demanded hospitalization.

But as of late, it had stopped working, and that terrified me. Each night I sat on my couch, twisting the edges of the afghan my mother had knitted twenty years earlier. I tugged the fringe, like my anxiety, tighter and tighter, winding the strands so they wouldn't come apart. I drank more, washing down the Vicodin my body now screamed for. But even then I couldn't get any relief.

12. *Sometimes things happen that terrify me. (True)*

Halloween night, the I.C.U. nurse called and said to come quick, it looked like it was time for him to go. I sped over streets slick with rain to the hospital and jogged through empty fluorescent halls to the I.C.U. Outside my father's room, I put on the thin rubber gloves and yellow paper gown I had been ordered to wear.

My father was unconscious and his left hand twitched, scratching the white sheet, dark tubes trailing behind like eels swimming in blue shadows of the room. He had suffered in this room for a month, intubated with a coiling tube strapped to his face, its flesh-colored plastic like the kind in Hannibal Lecter's mask. I tried to count the needles and tubes crammed into his nose, throat, arms, urethra, and gave up. I placed my hand over his, but sequestered behind a sheath of rubber, I was separated from my father's touch.

When I had visited earlier, the tube down his throat prevented speech, but his blue eyes sparked and he grasped my hand tighter than ever before. The other hand, tubes dangling, gestured in a made-up sign language I couldn't understand. He raised his arm chest level and arched his hand in a fluttering movement like a bird. I blurted out guesses, not bothering to consider whether they made any sense.

"How was my flight?"

He shook his head no.

"You had pigeon for dinner?"

His face crumpled in grim amusement, then he resorted to writing letters in the air with his fingertip, spelling out words, but I couldn't follow those, either. He let his hand drop to the bed with a flop. I feared my first guess was close, that he signed about one of us going away, but I couldn't venture that aloud. I didn't have a tube in my mouth, but I couldn't speak, either. Instead I held his hand and we stared into each other's eyes, making up for the words we never said.

But he didn't die. Actually, he got better. They removed the breathing tube, and then the feeding tube. He moved to a regular hospital room, then hospice.

"Your father survived the infection, but he's still dying," said his rumpled doctor.

"I know." I heard myself sounding defensive.

"Hospice will do everything they can to keep him comfortable, but I'm not going to lie to you. Your father will experience significant pain."

I nodded, thinking back two years earlier, before the cancer appeared and began its campaign of destruction. He had slipped in the garage and broken his hip. Nurses confided to me, in hushed tones with traces of accusation, that my father had an extremely low pain threshold. What did that mean, anyway, I had demanded. Sure they could measure outward manifestations of experience for a career full of patients, but how could they feel what another person felt? How did they know? Maybe it really feels more painful for him, I had said. They shook their heads and shot each other knowing glances. I didn't understand, their eyes said. I didn't know the things they knew.

13. *My judgment feels better than ever. (False)*

A month later, at hospice, I sat with my dad. As of that morning, he had a private room because his roommate had died (loudly, according to my father) at 3:06 A.M. in the bed five feet away. The man's body sat there until two morning-shift orderlies wheeled it past my father as he sat propped up in bed, trying to swallow lukewarm tea and runny eggs. We sat, not speaking, until my father broke the silence.

"I want to ask you something." His voice rasped, his throat still raw from intubation.

"What, Dad?"

"A favor."

"Okay." I waited to hear what he could possibly need.

"I'm dying."

"Yeah, I know."

The room swelled with silence.

"I want you to help me."

"Sure, Dad. Anything. Just tell me what you need."

"I want you to..." his throat chafed, making me wince. "I want you to help me die."

"What?"

His eyes closed and I watched his throat move as he swallowed.

"Kill me. I want you to kill me, honey." He paused. "Please."

"Jesus, Dad."

"There's a way to do it. You won't get in trouble."

"That's not exactly my biggest concern."

He didn't answer. I sat still, trying to think of what to say.

"Can I think about it, Dad?"

He closed his eyes and lay incredibly still, his chest barely rising with his breath. Then he opened his eyes and stared as if he couldn't quite place me.

"Sure." He closed his eyes again. "But don't take too long."

I sat in stunned silence, staring at the floor. When I looked up, he was asleep.

The request gnawed my stomach as I drove home. I wanted to do right here, but what was right? Follow the rules and let my father suffer a pain I couldn't imagine? Or kill him? Could I live with myself if I did this? Could I live with myself if I didn't? At home I poured a drink. It was asking a hell of a lot. But that was why I had to do it. How didn't matter. I would figure that part out later.

I had made my decision but still couldn't sleep. I tossed and turned and doubt swelled inside my throat. Who was I kidding? Right or wrong, there was no way I could go through with this.

14. I know that I am loved and there will always be someone who cares for me. (False)

The next morning, hospice called. They were sorry to inform me that my father had passed away. He died peacefully, they lied.

I made arrangements. My father wanted to be cremated, no funeral, no wake, saving the humiliation of a low turnout. A single parent and taciturn to the point of rudeness, my father had few friends. Those he'd had died before him or were themselves too sick to leave their beds. He was a widower and an only child, so that left just me.

"Looks like you're down to just one person in this world," Frank had said when he rode out of my life for good.

"Fuck you," I shot back. It was a shitty thing to say, calculated to hit hard and reverberate to the tips of my nerve endings. But he was right.

And now I was down to none. Now I was an orphan. Thirty years old maybe, but an orphan nonetheless. And it was in that selfish moment of untethered fear, panic in having no one at all, that everything unraveled.

15. When things go wrong, I feel like giving up. (True)

I couldn't sleep. I could not stop thinking about my father. It pained me to not know where he was, whether he was all right. Dr. Nguyen prescribed Ambien, Xanax, Valium. I swallowed the pills, grateful for Dr. Nguyen's generosity, and lay down with my frayed afghan to pray for rest.

16. My father was a good man. (True)

I saw my father standing in the driveway as I pulled in, home early from work. He stood there in a crisp white shirt, pressed khakis, tasseled brown loafers. Tan and spry, his eyes twinkled like he was up to something. Then I blinked and he disappeared.

I woke that night from coerced sleep and stepped through shadows to the bathroom. A breeze lifted the tiny hairs on the back of my neck and I asked the darkness, "Dad?" But he didn't answer.

"Dad, if you're there, say something." I stood frozen in the hall, waiting. "Dad, I want to talk to you. I promise I won't be scared."

I walked back from the bathroom, still searching for signs of him, but there was nothing. When I crawled back into bed I spoke the truth to the darkness, inviting him to appear in my driveway looking happy and fit.

"Those are words I haven't used to describe you in years, Dad. What made you such a model of stability? You stood at the stove frying hamburger patties, browning Tater Tots. Every night you had us at the dinner table at six sharp. You asked about my day. Did I need help with homework? Money for school supplies? If you drank, it was only in moderation. How could you stop at just one glass of burgundy? A single can of Budweiser? You were a good man. How can I possibly be your daughter?"

A knife-like sob stopped my eulogy. I rocked back and forth, crying in my private little vortex of tragedy.

"Daddy don't leave me," I whispered over and over, until I finally fell into the soft forgiving fog of sleep.

17. I'm as motivated to work as I ever was. (False)

A shrill noise rippled inside my ears, rolling waves through my head. The sound rose, gathered shape, and I recognized the ring of a phone. I mumbled into the receiver.

"Janet? Is that you?" said a voice.

I moved my lips and tongue to form words but choked and slipped into coughs.

"Janet?"

I dropped the phone and coughed until I caught my breath. I recognized my bed, and sunlight peaking through blinds.

"Janet, are you there? It's Diane...from the office?...Godammit, will you say something please? The court called. Again. You missed all of your morning appearances. The presiding judge talked to Henry." There was a long pause. "Henry's pissed, Janet."

I eased myself into a sitting position. My crotch felt damp and I thought I had peed myself, but the wetness inside my flannels was thick, sticky and I realized it was blood. The stain seeped from my crotch into the sheet, enormous and pure crimson. It reminded me of a crime scene.

"Did you hear what I said?"

"Tell him I'm sick." My throat felt like I had been drinking sand.

"We've been telling him that for two months. No one in this office wants to cover your appearances anymore and you knew damn well you were supposed to show up today."

I had nothing to say.

"The presiding judge is reporting you to the state bar and Henry said he's got no choice but to fire you."

The voice stopped talking and I hung up and went back to sleep. Day became night, then day again. Or maybe it was one endless day. I woke up to peek inside the refrigerator, have a drink, take a pill, then went back to sleep. First I lost days. Then weeks.

18. I have uncontrollable fits of laughter and tears. (True)

By December, Dr. Nguyen said he couldn't help me anymore and passed me off to a colleague, Dr. Blume.

Warm stereo speakers piped "Soft Rock from the '70s" into the antiseptic reception area where I listened to Jackson Browne, Elton John, and ABBA, hoping like hell this Blume could relieve the throbbing assault at the back of my skull. I listened to those songs the year my mother disappeared, the year I tumbled down an icy black abyss. Tapping my foot, I decided oldies comfort us because we can hear a song from twenty years ago, unfiltered by the nerve-searing shit we were going through at the time. The haze of nostalgia gave the gift of knowing that one particular period of hell was finally over.

I pondered this as John Denver sang "Annie's Song." My father bought me that album in an unprecedented retail therapy spree after my mother took off. I played it to make him happy, but I'd hated it. It depressed me that millions of people heard those clichéd lyrics as some shiny expression of love. This insight had made me feel even more alone. I must have been an odd kid.

I started crying then, but the fact that I was in a waiting room bawling over "Annie's Song" seemed funny somehow. A giggle escaped, then shifted into howls of laughter. I couldn't stop. I doubled over. It scared the shit out of me.

My laughter melted back into gasping sobs. I slid out of my chair onto the smooth industrial carpeting, the hard floor hurting my tailbone. As I wondered what the hell was wrong with me, a section of beige wall opened and a nurse appeared.

"The doctor will see you now."

19. I often dream about things best kept to myself. (True)

I'm sitting alone with my father on a metal bench in a deserted stadium covered in snow. A hidden sun emits gray light, turning the snow to ash. We wear hats, gloves, and parkas but still shiver. A snowflake falls on my face and warms my cheek. My father sits motionless, but not waiting, the way he waited his whole life. His body doesn't lurch with currents of pain and in this moment I don't worry.

But a shifting burdens my peace. Necessity. A need for words. I summon courage to speak, to say what I need to say. I'm holding a rectangular eyeglass case and the lines etched on it match the corrugated lines on the bench where I sit by my father, our knees touching. My father points to the case. He looks into my eyes and reaches for it, then grips it with surprising strength.

"Don't." I tug it back, but he won't let go. He holds on, pulling with unfamiliar insistency as tendons clench in my neck. I'm not sad about what I have to tell him. I only want to inflict the least amount of pain.

"Dad…" I stop.

Tell me, his eyes say. Tell me what you need to say.

"Dad, I did it." I gesture with the case. "I'm dead. These are my ashes." As if on cue, a fleck of my former self escapes through the seam. It swirls upward with the snow and then disappears.

My father's face contorts like it did the day my mother died and his mouth croaks out words. "No. Undo it. Undo it right now." He shoves me off the bench and I start to fall.

I wake as my body hits my bedroom floor. I'm gasping for air and crawl up to snap on the lamp to erase the dream. The mess of empty amber bottles on the nightstand reminds me what's real. What the fuck have I done?

I dial the phone and hear a voice. "911 operator, what's your emergency?"

When the ambulance comes, a paramedic shines a light in my eyes, asks me my name, what did I take?

He is young. Handsome, with eyes flecked in gold. He touches my arm and I grip his hand, holding it there, not willing to feel him let go. "You're okay," he says. "You're going to make it through."

And in that moment, all I want is to believe him. ◆

Elena Ferrante

THE FACTORY

(translated by Ann Goldstein)

In the factory—she had immediately understood—overwork drove people to want to have sex not with their wife or husband in their own house, where they returned exhausted and empty of desire, but there, at work, morning or afternoon. The men reached out their hands at every opportunity, they propositioned you if they merely passed by; and women, especially the ones who were not so young, laughed, rubbed against them with their big bosoms, fell in love, and love became a diversion that mitigated the labor and the boredom, giving an impression of real life.

From Lila's first days the men had tried to get close, as if to sniff her. Lila repulsed them, and they laughed or went off humming songs full of obscene allusions. One morning, to make things perfectly clear, she almost pulled off the ear of a man who passing by had made a lewd remark and pressed a kiss on her neck. He was a fairly attractive man in his forties, named Edo, who spoke to everyone in an allusive way and was good at telling dirty jokes. Lila grabbed the ear with one hand and twisted it, pulling with all her strength, her nails digging into the membrane, without letting go her grip even though the man was yelling, as he tried to parry the kicks she was giving him. After which, furious, she went to see Bruno Soccavo to protest.

Lila had seen him only a few times since he hired her—fleetingly, without paying him much attention. In that situation, however, she was able to observe him closely. He was standing behind the desk; he had risen deliberately, the way men do when a woman enters the room. Lila was amazed: Soccavo's face was bloated, his eyes shrouded by dissipation, his chest heavy, and his flushed complexion clashed like magma against his black hair and the white of his wolfish teeth. She wondered: what does this man have to do with the young man, the friend of Nino who was studying law? And she felt there was no continuity between the time on Ischia and the sausage factory: between them stretched a void, and in the leap from one space to the other Bruno—maybe because his father had been ill recently and the weight of the business (the debts, some said) had fallen suddenly on his shoulders—had changed for the worse.

She told him her complaints, he began to laugh.

"Lina," he warned her, "I did you a favor, but don't make trouble for me. We all work hard here, don't always have your gun aimed: people have to relax every so often, otherwise it causes problems for me."

"The rest of you can relax with each other."

He ran his eyes over her with a look of amusement.

"I thought you liked to joke."

"I like it when I decide."

Lila's hard tone made him change his. He became serious, he said without looking at her: you're the same as ever—so beautiful in Ischia. Then he pointed to the door: go to work, go on.

But from then on, when he met her in the factory, he never failed to speak to her in front of everyone, and he always gave her a good-humored compliment. That familiarity in the end sanctioned Lila's situation in the factory: she was in the good graces of the young Soccavo, and so it was as well to leave her alone. This seemed to be confirmed when one afternoon, right after the lunch break, a large woman named Teresa stopped her and said teasingly: you're wanted in the seasoning room. Lila went into the big room where the salamis were drying, a rectangular space crammed with salamis hanging from the ceiling in the yellow light. There she found Bruno, who appeared to be doing an inspection but in reality wanted to chat.

While he wandered around the room poking and sniffing with the air of an expert, he asked her about Pinuccia, her sister-in-law, and—a thing that irritated Lila—said, without looking at her, in fact as he examined a soppressata: she was never happy with your brother, she fell in love with me that summer, like you and Nino. Then he passed by and, with his back to her, added: it was thanks to her that I discovered that pregnant women love to make love. Then, without giving her the time to comment or make a sarcastic remark or get angry, he stopped in the middle of the room and said that while the place as a whole had nauseated him ever since he was a child, here in the drying room he had always felt comfortable, there was something satisfying, solid, the product that was nearly finished, acquiring refinement, spreading its odor, being readied for the market. Look, touch it, he said to her, it's compact, hard, smell the fragrance it gives off: it's like the odor of man and woman when they embrace and touch—you like it?—if you knew how many girls I've brought here since I was a boy. And just then he grabbed her by the waist, slid his lips down her long neck, as he squeezed her bottom—he seemed to have a hundred hands, he was rubbing her on top of the apron, underneath it, at a frenetic and breath-less speed, in an exploration without pleasure, a pure intrusive desire.

For Lila everything, except the smell of the salamis, reminded her of Stefano's violence and for several seconds she felt annihilated, she was afraid of being murdered. Then fury seized her, and she hit Bruno in the face and between the legs, she yelled at him, you are a shit of a man, you've got nothing down there; come here, pull it out so I can cut it off, you shit.

Bruno let go, retreated. He touched his lip, which was bleeding, he snickered in embarrassment, he mumbled: I'm sorry, I thought there might be at least a little gratitude. Lila shouted at him: You mean I have to pay a penalty, or you'll fire me, is that it? He laughed again, shook his head: No, if you don't want to you don't want to, that's all, I apologized, what else should I do? But she was beside herself, only now did she begin to feel on her body the traces of his hands, and she knew it would last, it wasn't something she could wash off with soap. She backed up toward the door, she said to him: You were lucky right now, but whether you fire me or not, I swear I'll make you curse the moment you touched me. As she was leaving he muttered: What did I do to you, I didn't do anything, come here, as if these were real problems, let's make peace.

She went back to her job. At the time she was working in the steamy vat room, as a kind of attendant who among other things was supposed to keep the floor dry, a fruitless task. Edo, the one whose ear she had almost torn off, looked at her with curiosity. All of them, men and women, kept their eyes on her as she returned, enraged, from the drying room. Lila didn't exchange a glance with anyone. She grabbed a rag, slammed it down on the bricks, and began to wipe the floor, which was a swamp, uttering aloud, in a threatening tone: Let's see if some other son of a bitch wants to try. Her companions concentrated on their work.

For days she expected to be fired, but she wasn't. If she happened to run into Bruno, he smiled kindly, she responded with a cold nod. No consequences, then, except disgust at those short hands, and flashes of hatred. But since Lila continued to show the same contemptuous indifference toward the supervisors, they suddenly began to torment her again, by constantly changing her job, forcing her to work until she was worn out, making obscene remarks. A sign that they had been given permission.

She didn't tell Enzo anything about almost tearing off the ear, about Bruno's attack, about the everyday harassments and struggles. If he asked her how things were going at the sausage factory, she answered sarcastically: Why don't you tell me how it is where you work? And since he was silent, Lila teased him a little and then together they turned to the exercises for the correspondence course. They took refuge there for many reasons, the most important being to avoid questions about the future: what were they to each other, why was he taking care of her and Gennaro, why did she accept it, why had they been living together for so long while Enzo waited in vain every night for her to join him, tossing and turning in the bed, going to the kitchen with the excuse of getting a drink of water, glancing at the door with the frosted glass to see if she had turned off the light yet and look at her shadow. Mute tensions—I knock, I let him enter—his doubts, hers. In the end they preferred to dull their senses by competing with block diagrams as if they were equipment for gymnastics.

"Let's do the diagram of the door opening," Lila said.

"Let's do the diagram of knotting the tie," Enzo said.

"Let's do the diagram of tying Gennaro's shoes," Lila said.

"Let's do the diagram of making coffee in the *napoletana*," Enzo said.

From the simplest actions to the most complicated, they racked their brains to diagram daily life, even if the Zurich tests didn't require it. And not because Enzo wanted to but because, as usual, Lila, who had begun diffidently, grew more and more excited each day, and now, in spite of the cold at night, she was frantic to reduce the entire wretched world they lived in to the truth of zeroes and ones. She seemed to aspire to an abstract linearity—the abstraction that bred all abstractions—hoping that it would assure her a restful tidiness.

"Let's diagram the factory," she proposed one evening.

"The whole process?" he asked, bewildered.

"Yes."

He looked at her, he said: "All right, let's start with your job."

An irritated scowl crossed her face; she said good night, and went to her room. ◆

[§29 of *Those Who Leave and Those Who Stay*,
Book Three of the Neapolitan Novels,
Europa Editions]

Huang Lihai

STREET

(translated by Song Zijiang)

what is an acceptable object of belief
a person here
will quickly be drowned by the noise of the city
he wishes to have the grand square
to be his paddock
but he can't, this afternoon,
his anger, it still seems excessive

this afternoon, a negligible person
across a street
walks steadfastly forward
heart headed towards matters across the way

George Choundas

FOR YOU, CITY, FOR YOU

He skims the east curb. His skin is ambiguous, the color of a wallet. Perhaps he brought it from another hemisphere. Perhaps he simply enjoyed sports as a child.

There are emissions, do not doubt it: from right rear a spongy squeak like stale popcorn fighting; from underneath something metal and cantankerous. He stands easy on the pedals.

On the sidewalk the slow ones look down, the fast ones forward. There is a different vernal equinox, lasting three days or four, very sweet, during which there are tourists enough they are picked out instantly but not so many that tracking them makes him dizzy. It has come and well gone. The clouds wheel on him a little.

At the next intersection, two girls. They put their bodies in a way that wants to show they do not depend on each other. He slows. They are on his left as he approaches. His shoulders are back and relaxed and challenging. The girls look up but not at him. On a volume basis, his gaze is the least returned in the city.

The first girl he passes, the northerly, looks at last. But now she lifts her hand to her chest and waggles and drops it. She does this as if to say, Look, you know the drill, you know we do not want a ride in your pedicab, you know I will say no, and you know I will use some kind of hand gesture, and because you know all of this already I will do the last as indifferently as possible.

This only incites him. Still standing, he stops. Directly in front of the waggling girl.

Free ride, he tells her.

Northerly is pleasant-looking, but plainer than her patently beautiful friend, who is taller by a skull.

Free ride, he repeats.

She looks at him, then away at nothing and back again.

Free?

Free, no charge.

She smiles uncertainly. This he understands to be a cue.

Really, no charge, he says. Come on, for you, free.

The string of words tricks out a flicker of accent. Two of them reveal an imported chivalry, sly and profligate. If he enjoyed a childhood sport it was soccer.

She raises her eyebrows at Southerly, who does not react especially. He seizes on the pause.

On one condition, he says, slow enough to imply it was planned all along. If I make you laugh, I take you out to dinner.

He is comfortable with idiom. A foreigner then, but not lately.

What?

Yes. If I make you laugh, even once, I buy you dinner. If you don't laugh, then no dinner. He holds her eyes, blinking only once his long lashes.

This time she does not look at her friend. She speaks their destination as a question, gets a nod and a second blink (a wink?), and settles into the pedicab. He watches, half turned in his seat. Her friend follows, pausing to look where she will place her ass before placing it. This, he has seen, is something only the self-regarding and the self-effacing do with their asses.

They move west, into the general orange of sunset. It is crosstown a number of avenues. The breeze is steady because his pace is steady. His path is not. Each time a car ahead goes recalcitrant, he veers toward one side, as if to complain to its fellows parked there, and just before he gives one of these a nice dent for not helping he veers streetward again, pulling into a corridor not visible before. He makes co-workers of centimeters.

Northerly wonders why his calves are not a bigger deal. Rather than protrude they are simply solid, creditable without casting outward for credit, pistons in their sheaths. She expects him to turn around so he can crack a joke, or make a face, or simply look back charmingly or impishly or goadingly or quizzically. He does none of these. In fact as he pedals he spends much of his time looking about, at sky and storefronts, as if he were on holiday, the pedicab a hatbox.

He slows. They have arrived. The girls step onto the sidewalk. Still he does not look at them. Northerly comes around to face him.

You didn't make me laugh, she says.

Make you laugh? His mouth stays open. *You* were supposed to make *me* laugh.

What? You said—

Make me laugh or I buy you dinner, this is what I said. And look— he crosses his arms like a big baby, tucking hands into armpits—I don't even think about laughing.

She laughs.

Got you, he says, grinning broadly. He gives the sides of her shoulders a slow, deliberate two-handed pat.

I want my money back, she says.

Now he laughs.

Got you, she says, waggling this time her head in vague caricature and giving his shoulders the same double pat. She fights down a smile as her hands out-bounce in a pantomime of recoil.

Write down your address. Pick you up tomorrow night, seven-thirty.

Steadily she takes from her purse a piece of paper and writes on it and gives it to him.

Dress comfortable, he says. Tomorrow you're driving.

She laughs. He pulls his machine toward him.

You laughed a second time, he says, getting on. Now it's dinner and breakfast.

You wish, she says, allowing herself a giggle. She grabs onto her friend and starts walking.

He pedals slowly. Standing. Backward. Now, forward. He is underway as he calls out.

I like bacon with my eggs.

They are moving exactly apart. For looking they use the air over their shoulders. They speak to each other but call to the city.

What about names with your addresses?

Slow down, beautiful—he speeds up—Let's take this slow.

Katharine Coles

WAY/WARD

Sally for any direction you name
Or not. After, back, in, too

Out to follow. Down
Like a dog or some hero

Sunk into his own private
Guided tour of hell. Some of us,

Cowed, go home and weave.
Others take to sea to find

How many animal shapes
Contain them. I might have

A horn on my nose or more
Arms than I can tell what

To do and as many brains, odd
Numbers of hearts

That won't be led. Good
Heaven, do unto or just feed them—

I'd rather think what greens
Mean in numbers or how

A sky's dazzle blinds
And blisses. East, west: no way

To know, is the thing, what
To count, how far to go.

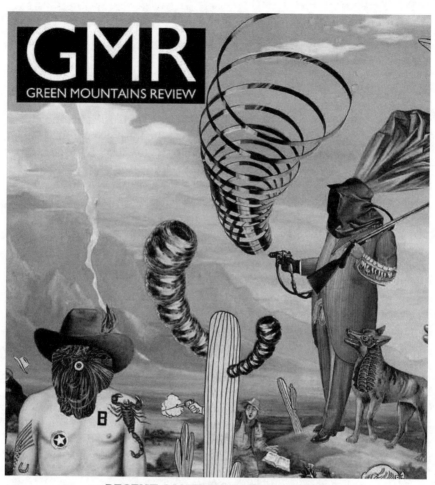

RECENT CONTRIBUTORS INCLUDE

Fiction: Kim Chinquee
Brian Evenson
Tao Greenfield
Lee Ann Roripaugh
Luke B. Goebel
Lou Beach

Poetry: Tony Hoagland
Julianna Baggott
Olena Kalytiak Davis
Major Jackson
Matthew Lippman
Joshua Marie Wilkinson

Hadar Bar-Nadav
Emilia Phillips
Elizabeth Bradfield
Cynthia Huntington
Melissa Broder

www.greenmountainsreview.com

Izaac Jenks

SATURN RETURN

Muffled thunder beyond the foothills caused Jesse to stop digging and look up at the sky. He thrust his spade into the fresh pile of dirt at his feet, took his gloves off and put them in the back pocket of his jeans, and pulled off his sweaty T-shirt, mopped his face with it, and draped it over the handle of the spade. The cool air against his skin made him feel like a photograph of himself in a tray of developer. He picked up his canteen, took a long drink, then set the canteen down. He pressed his hands on the small of his back and twisted to stretch the kinks out of his spine. Clouds were moving toward him from the mountains. Gray vapor poured over a ridge between two truncated peaks which looked to Jesse like the silhouette of a crouching sumo wrestler.

It was late in the afternoon. Jesse had been digging for maybe an hour this last stint, singing as loud as he could, to keep the oxygen pumping into his muscles, old Stones and Beatles songs, and Dylan, and Bob Marley, and the Dead. Whenever he forgot the lyrics, he made up his own, the raunchier the better.

Jesse realized he wouldn't be able to finish this section of the ditch before it got dark. The Indian summer weather had lulled him into thinking he'd have a couple more hours of daylight, but what with the cloud cover gathering and the sun disappearing behind the mountains, he'd barely have enough light to make it back to his truck. The truck was parked about four miles away, beyond a huddle of low hills, and the route he'd have to negotiate to get there crossed two creeks, with half a mile of stony scrubland between them, then followed a fence-line along a ridge that narrowed to less than a yard in some places. The drive back to the crew shack, in Choteau, would take another thirty minutes on top of that.

Jesse unscrewed the cap from his thermos and swallowed the last mouthful of coffee. It was barely lukewarm. He spat out the grounds stuck to his tongue and took out his tobacco and rolled a cigarette against his thigh and lit it. No, there was at least another day's worth of digging before the ditch would reach the deeper cut the crew had made with a backhoe, hauled by highway and over logging roads on a flatbed and then driven in, from the other direction—all told about ninety miles as the crow wouldn't fly—earlier in the week. This feeder section was on too steep a slope, and followed too erratic a line, to be dug with the machine.

Jesse had volunteered to finish the feeder ditch solo; he got along fine with the other guys and with the boss, it wasn't that, but he persuaded himself that a few days alone with a purely physical task to perform would be enjoyable, somehow spiritually beneficial. Not that anyone cared what his reasons were. Jesse was what they would have called a "dreamer," if they thought about him at all, but he had proven himself a reliable worker, and they knew they could trust him not to goof off too much.

He had recently started going to a meditation group that met in Helena, led by this tall guy with a soft Oklahoma accent, who had won him over at the first session. Sitting on his buckwheat *zafu*, legs crossed, eyes closed, the guy had said,

> When you meditate, imagine your mind is like a city in the middle of the day, with noise coming at you from all directions. That's your conscious mind using most of its energy to fight with itself, your thoughts all trying to win arguments with all your other thoughts. You want to try to quell those disputes gradually, deepen your meditation by degrees. First, imagine subtracting the noise of all the trucks—the delivery vans, the garbage trucks, the construction trucks full of steel beams and heavy chains and drums of solvents, clanging and clattering. Bit by bit, as they vanish, the city is measurably quieter, but still full of noise. Then take away all the sirens, the police cars and the fire trucks and the ambulances. Then subtract all the taxis, their motors and horns, their doors slamming. Now subtract all the other cars, all the revving engines and the tires rolling against the pavement and the radios blaring. Next filter out all the people, their talking and shouting and laughing, their coughing and sneezing, and then their footsteps, and the city is a lot quieter but also full of new noises, which you hadn't noticed before, because they were buried beneath the louder, more insistent ones. Now you can hear the air conditioners, dogs barking, birds, sometimes even the sound of the wind....

Jesse was at an intoxicatingly rudimentary stage in his own spiritual practice, and was still young enough to find deeply attractive the notion of ascending into a state of no-mindedness, gleefully flinging into his conception of it all the emotional detritus—the rejections, the failures, the indignities, the mortifications—that had accumulated in the duct-taped old footlocker of his self-image. Austerity! Simplicity! Emancipation from possessions! He'd even gone so far as to swear off women, since breaking up with his girlfriend last year, in Chicago, after she hooked up with his best friend. What could he do? At least they'd had the decency to tell him in person, though it had seemed the opposite of thoughtful at the time. He still couldn't figure out whose had been the worse betrayal. To top it off, his parents were after him to finally go back to grad school, but he couldn't face that decision yet.

With unconscious clarity, he'd taken refuge in Montana, where he'd never been before, the most male, least academic place on his mental map.

Shortly after the breakup, he'd gone on a retreat at a Trappist monastery in Kentucky, to visit a friend who was a novice monk there. But the Abbot had forbidden them to get together until Jesse's final day—Trappists took a vow of silence, and a visit from a chum was no excuse for breaking it—except for a few minutes the morning he arrived. Matt had looked forlorn and pale and underfed in his coarse brown robe but said things were going O.K. Well, that could mean anything. Meanwhile, Jesse was installed for the week in the retreat house, and was free to attend the hours—he ended up sampling them all; Vespers (at the end of the day) and especially Vigils (deep in the night, and with the most haunting chants) were his favorites—and to walk in the woods and fields around the monastery.

His second night there, walking back from the chapel after Vigils, Jesse had startled a pheasant out of the stubble of a harvested field, a whooshing explosion of muscles and feathers accompanied by a peculiar oscillatory shrilling, like screeches braided with chirps and pulled rapidly into the distance, that had reminded him of the sound of the iron wheel of his grandfather's wheelbarrow grinding against the axle when the wheelbarrow was pushed along filled with rocks or bricks or topsoil. The wheelbarrow had blotches of dried concrete in the hopper, left from the years when his grandfather and his father had built their houses. They scraped him when he'd sat or knelt in the wheelbarrow, gripping the rounded lip along its edges and bouncing up and down as his father gave him rides over the bumpy terrain of their back yard when he was three and four, *straining his back all those years carpentering and endlessly planting his beloved trees, driving out beyond the city limits early every spring when it was still cold and hiking into the woods and hauling back choice saplings, rootballs wrapped in burlap filling the trunk, then digging holes and mixing peat moss and soil and hauling the swaddled plants around the yard in the wheelbarrow and nestling them in and lugging buckets of water and pouring it into the mounds of dirt and tamping down the slurry with a spade, the wheelbarrow shafts square oak tapering into rounded handles like oars smoothed glassy, generations of calluses that must have been, flowing into my genes from both tributaries, I guess, definitely farming ancestors and probably seafarers, too, chunky dories and possibly whaleboats, fragiler and tippier, what a life, Jee-zus, so much for Lamarck, none of that nautical DNA got passed down to me, I ain't no aspiring giraffe stickin' his neck out for nothin', perspiring more like, never article myself off to that grim confinement, no sir, no press gang frog-marchin' me out of some grog shop, there's no escape, none, give me the mountains any day, terra firma under my feet, "Halp! Halp! Cap'n Albatross, get me off this friggin' tub," perpetual stench belowdecks, scurvy buggers stacked up soused in their wank pits, verminous oatmeal and ship's biscuit like wafers of shale and utter thralldom to the whims of tyrants and their diabolical punishments, flogging and knouting and keel-hauling, not* (as he'd naïvely imagined the first time he encountered the term) *dragging a man behind the ship by a rope for a few minutes, ordeal enough that would be, but lowering him spraddled upfacing and naked down the prow, arms and legs tied to ropes held taut by shipmates and walked along the length of the moving vessel, grating him over the ragged timbers and the barnacles and keelworms and mussels fouling the hull, hellish way to kill a guy, what kind of worse than beasts are we, way beyond sadistic, snakes eating snakes even when they're not hungry.... and Pop's brother Uncle Henry* (a.k.a. Uncle Hungry, for his love of pancakes especially) *one day when he was a kid sliding down a post in the garage and getting a long, ugly splinter up his belly and Gramps fetching pliers and pulling it out, gruff old geezer even before he was old, crinkled eyes and fine white hair tousled by the breeze, standing in his overalls and white shirt lost in abstraction in his blackberry patch... and that summer afternoon when I was thirteen and Pop was getting the car keys to drive me to the doctor's for my camp physical and we hear screams from the house across the street where this kid Sean whose parents and brothers aren't home is roughhousing with their fool mutt and somehow the dog breaks loose from its stake and tears around the yard yapping like crazy and Sean chases after him and the hook of the dog's chain gouges through Sean's ankle and locks around a tendon, stringy white cord in the bloodless hole scooped in his flesh, and Pop gets him and carries him to the car, chain and all, and drives to the doctor's and carries him in and screams emanate from the examining room and the nurse bustles around, then quiet and Sean limps out, his foot wrapped in a bandage, the nurse carrying his shoe, and the doc gestures for Pop to come in with me and closes the door and tells me to take my clothes off and has the stethoscope tucked into the waistband of his pants to keep it warm and listens to my chest and gags me with a tongue depressor and pokes that flashlight cone in my ears and palpates my stomach and all the rest of it and at the end standing there with my underpants pulled down Pop sitting in a chair beside the desk the doc perched on a stool starts rolling my balls around in his fingers and I sprout a hard-on face flaming what the fuck can't believe it but neither of them reacts or says a word must happen all the time and then I get dressed and Pop drives Sean home but his ordeal isn't over yet, later that night screams again when Sean's goon of a father returns and hears what he hears and yanks his belt off and roars and starts whipping Sean's ass for the felonies he's committed that day, Christ the fathers some guys are saddled with* and a blizzard of other thoughts.

Jesse had got pretty scratched up himself once on the rocks along the shore of Mt. Desert Island, in Maine, one afternoon when he succumbed to a dare by a fellow student in the summer program at the genetics lab there. Smart kids from all over the country. He and this guy Michael, from Lock Haven, Pennsylvania, were wandering along the boulder piles at the base of a bluff near the mansion the lab used as a dorm for the high-school students, and Michael had squatted down and scrutinized a tumultuous cove maybe thirty feet across and studded with menacing snaggles of granite. The water was very cold, as it always is in Maine, and surged and slopped three, four, five feet up the jumble of shore rocks.

Michael began coaxing Jesse to jump in, to his objection they'd be battered to bits insisting "No, look" and tossing a twig out into the swell. "Any given water molecule stays in the same place—it's the wave energy, not the water itself, that's in motion," and he was right, the twig did stay put, and the stately, mysterious mechanics of it, the molecules' headlong frolics somehow dissipating in the aggregate mêlée, began to emerge from the chaos of Jesse's fear.

Michael took off his sneakers and his shirt, emptied the pockets of his shorts, and, saying "Watch!" and holding his nose and canting his legs like a marionette, leaped out over the water and sploshed in, his pale flesh dimming out of focus in the greenish brine before he resurfaced right where he'd gone under, eyes red-rimmed and teeth clicking, dog-paddling energetically as waves higher than his head rolled past. Michael's bravado as much as his physics persuaded Jesse, so he, too, stripped down and threw himself into the water. The shock of the cold was instantaneous—every part of him was freezing, even his hair—and Jesse bobbed in place as unmolested by the sea as the twig had been.

What Michael's analysis had failed to account for, though, was the fate of the wave energy when it finally reached something immovable—namely, the shore rocks, whose barnacles were as sharp as razors, and, enmeshed in the violent surge and ebb, the boys got thoroughly sliced up in their struggle to clamber ashore. Once the numbness wore off, the cuts on Jesse's torso and limbs began to sting like jellyfish welts, with a pain that left an odd metallic taste on the edges of his tongue, and as they made their way in silence back up the bluff toward the mansion, he felt as if he'd won some challenging contest but in a manner that was worse than defeat.

Michael lost interest in Jesse in the days after the incident, and moved on to playing his mind games with other students. Michael was kicked out of the program a couple of weeks later; the counselors wouldn't let on exactly why. Jesse wondered what had become of him. *Och, if only we'd culled ye Meek, ye mate huff steed!* Maybe he'd ridden off down the coast on the back of an obliging seahorse...

Jesse started to gather up his tools while he smoked, clinching the cigarette between his lips to keep his hands free. The wind shifted as it always does at twilight and blew smoke in his eyes, and he squeezed them shut. What eternities the fractions of eternity contain! He dropped his cigarette in the ditch and rubbed his eyes; the moment he opened them and saw her, Jesse got a pungent whiff of the approaching bear. She had moved out of an avalanche chute and down through the patches of sage on the slope, and had been downwind of him till the wind reversed. She was coming toward him at a steady pace, her head lolling from side to side but her eyes, as if held in twin gimbals, unwaveringly locked on him. Jesse's mouth went as dry as a kiln in the desert, and an icy-warm floating sensation blossomed in his groin and his brain.

The grizzly was about seventy yards away, and with weird detachment Jesse took in the heavy sheaths of fat she'd built up in the last few weeks of feeding, which shifted like gigantic rubber pancakes underneath her fur as she moved forward with a paradoxical litheness, like a Bengal tiger swaddled in five mink coats. She jumped across the transverse cut, which was about six feet wide, as if it were a garden hose, and slowed down as she reached the feeder ditch. The bear had pale-yellow eyes, set close together at the base of her snout, and her round furry ears made Jesse think of the ears on a Teddy bear.

Jesse's lungs felt devoid of breath, and then he sucked in air like a drowning man surrendering and letting the water flood in, and as the bear halted and rose up before him to her full height, a desperate vehemence arose in him, his voice found itself, and he began to sing,

> Perhaps it's the color of the sun cut flat
> Uncoverin' the crossroads I'm standing at,
> Or maybe it's the weather or somethin' like that,
> But Mama, you been on my mind . . .

and the bear dropped back onto her forepaws and stood as still as a cow in its stall, only tilting her head quizzically from time to time, and languidly blinking, and then, an inconvenient poverty having afflicted his repertoire, Jesse began the song again, standing with his arms held palms-out at his sides, instinctively looking not directly at the bear but at a scarlet patch of willow over her shoulder, feeling as weak and as strong as he'd ever felt in his life, and she was content with it and turned and walked off into the long blue shadow seeping down the slope.◆

CONTRIBUTORS' NOTES

DIANE HOOVER BECHTLER lives in Charlotte, N.C., with her husband, Michael Gross, who is a poet with a day job, and with their cat, Call Me IshMeow. As well as writing short work, she is working on a novel. She graduated summa cum laude in English from Queens University, where she later earned her M.F.A. She has published in *The Gettysburg Review, Thema Literary Journal, Everyday Fiction,* and *The Dead Mule, School of Southern Literature,* and other journals.

REBECCA BERNARD holds an M.F.A. from Vanderbilt University, where she served as a fiction and music editor for *Nashville Review.* Work appears in journals such as *Makeout Creek* and online at McSweeney's Internet Tendency. Currently lives and teaches in Louisville, Kentucky.

LUCY BIEDERMAN (lucybiederman.blogspot.com) is the author of four chapbooks of poetry. In 2013, she was nominated for a Pushcart Prize and was a finalist for the Best of the Net Prize. Her poetry has appeared in *BOMB, The Tusculum Review, The Laurel Review, Denver Quarterly, Unsplendid,* and other journals, and her fiction in *The Collagist.* She received an M.F.A. in poetry from George Mason University and is a doctoral student in English at the University of Louisiana–Lafayette.

STEVE BRADBURY'S translation of Hsia Yü's fourth collection of poetry, entitled *Salsa* (1999), was recently published by Zephyr Press.

ABE BRENNAN spent the first fifteen years of his adult life losing money in the music business. His prose has appeared in *The Iowa Review, The Normal School,* and *StoryQuarterly.* He lives in Denver.

TALLY BRENNAN's has published in journals including *Rosebud, 13th Moon, PMS/Poem, Memoir, Story, Room of One's Own, Kaleidoscope, Minetta Review, Meridian,* and online at JMWW, Hobo Pancake, and Lady Jane Miscellany. A story of hers was selected for inclusion in Writing Aloud, InterAct Theatre's series of readings by professional actors, and nominated for a Pushcart Prize. She is grateful to the Leeway Foundation, the Astraea Foundation, and the Five Counties Art Foundation (PA) for their support.

J. CAMP BROWN has received fellowships from Phillips Exeter Academy, where he was the George Bennett Writer-in-Residence, from the University of Arkansas, where he took his M.F.A., and from the Arkansas

Arts Council. His poems have previously appeared in journals such as *Memorious, Nashville Review, Tar River Poetry, RHINO,* and *The Louisville Review.* He hails from Fort Smith, AR.

ELIZABETH CANTWELL lives in Los Angeles with her husband, screenwriter Christopher Cantwell, and their son and small dog. She has a Ph.D. in Literature & Creative Writing from U.S.C., and her poetry has appeared in a variety of journals, including *PANK, Anti-, The Los Angeles Review,* and *The Literary Review.* Her book of poems, *Nights I Let the Tiger Get You* (Black Lawrence Press, 2014), was a finalist for the 2012 Hudson Prize; she is also the author of a chapbook, *Premonitions* (Grey Book Press, 2014). She teaches Humanities at The Webb Schools, in Claremont, CA.

GEORGE CHOUNDAS has published fiction and nonfiction in over twenty publications, including *The American Reader, Michigan Quarterly Review,* and *Subtropics.* He is author of *The Pirate Primer* and a former F.B.I. agent. He reported to the F.B.I. Academy at 196 pounds and was dismayed to learn the heaviest weight class in Defensive Tactics was "over 195." By Week Three, even his blood hurt. By Week Five, his bad ear was his good ear.

CHUN SUE (birth name: Zou Nan) was born in 1983. She lives in Beijing but originates from Shandong Province. Variously described as brutalist or edgy, her work has appeared in *Renmin Wenxue* (People's Literature), *Furong, Xiaoshuo Jie* (Fiction World), and *Shixuan Kan* (Poetry Selection Magazine). She is a feature writer for the magazine *Xin Zhoukan* (New Weekly). Her books include *Beijing Doll, Fun and Games,* and *Ray of Passion;* she edited the anthology *Poetry of the Post-80s Generation.*

TIA CLARK is from a square-mile town in Westchester, N.Y., and currently lives in Bloomington, Indiana, where she's completing an M.F.A. Her work has appeared in *American Short Fiction, FiveChapters, Fourteen Hills,* and *BLACKBERRY: a magazine.* She loves good sitcoms and laser tag.

KATHARINE COLES' fifth poetry collection, *The Earth Is Not Flat* (Red Hen, 2013), was written under the auspices of the National Science Foundation's Antarctic Artists and Writers Program. Recent work has appeared in *Poetry Northwest, Seneca Review, Virginia Quarterly Review, Image, Crazyhorse, Ascent,* and *Poetry;* ten poems, translated into German by Klaus Martens, appeared in the summer 2014 issue of *Matrix.* A professor at the University of Utah, in 2009-10 she served as the inaugural director of the Poetry Foundation's Harriet Monroe Poetry Institute. She has received grants and awards from the N.E.A., the N.E.H. and, in 2012-13, the Guggenheim Foundation.

CHRISTINA COOKE's fiction, poetry, and nonfiction centers on queer female perspectives from the Jamaican diaspora attempting to find solace and community. Her work has appeared or will appear in journals in the U.S., U.K., Canada, and the U.S. Virgin Islands, and in her chapbook *l'appel du vide* (Porkbelly Press, 2014). Follow her on Twitter @cjctlc. She has a bachelor's and a master's in English Literature with a Creative Writing focus, and is now a fiction student at the Iowa Writers' Workshop.

YANN CORIDIAN is a French filmmaker and a writer. He has written ten novels, many published by l'École des Loisirs. His first feature film, "Ouf," was released in theatres in February, 2013. He is currently completing his next screenplay.

KATIE CORTESE is the author of *Girl Power and Other Short-Short Stories* (ELJ Publications, 2015). Her work has recently appeared in *Gulf Coast, Blackbird, Day One,* and elsewhere. She teaches creative writing at Texas Tech, where she also serves as fiction editor of *Iron Horse Literary Review.*

CYNTHIA CRUZ is the author *Ruin* (Alice James Books), *The Glimmering Room* (Four Way Books), and *Wunderkammer* (in fall of 2014, Four Way Books). She has received fellowships from Yaddo and MacDowell as well as a Hodder Fellowship from Princeton. Her essays and art reviews have been published in the *LA Review of Books, The Rumpus,* and Hyperallergic. She teaches at Sarah Lawrence and lives in Brooklyn.

MAME EKBLOM CUDD has a B.A. in economics from Wells College and an M.S.S.W. from Columbia. She attended the Squaw Valley Community of Writers Conference (2009, 2011) and the Arizona State Writers conference (2006, 2007). Her work has appeared in *Broad River Review, SNReview, Fiction Magazine,* Crack the Spine, Fiction Fix, the Puritan, and other places.

JAMES D'AGOSTINO is the author of *Slur Oeuvre* (New Michigan Press) and *Nude With Anything* (New Issues Press). He directs the B.F.A. program in Creative Writing at Truman State University.

AARON DELEE has a B.A. in Creative Writing from Loyola University Chicago in 2005, and then received his M.F.A. in Creative Writing–Poetry in 2013 from Northwestern. His work has appeared in *Court Green,*

Interrobang, Mad Hatter's Review, and other places. When he's not reading or writing, he enjoys running along Chicago's lakefront path.

JENNIFER FEELEY's translations of poetry and essays from Chinese into English have been published in various literary journals and anthologies. Currently she is translating *Not Written Words,* selected poems by Sai Sai, for Zephyr Press. Her edited collection, *Simultaneous Worlds: Global Science Fiction Cinema,* is forthcoming in 2015.

ELENA FERRANTE was born in Naples, Italy. She is the author of *My Brilliant Friend, The Story of a New Name, The Days of Abandonment, Troubling Love,* and *The Lost Daughter,* all published by Europa Editions.

JASON FREURE has published poems in *Vallum, ditch, Echolocation, Maynard,* and *The Hart House Review.* His reviews and essays have appeared in *Lemon Hound* and *The Puritan.* He lives in Toronto and writes for the Town Crier blog.

LEORA FRIDMAN is the author of *Precious Coast* (H_ngm_n B_ _ks), *On the architecture* and *Essential Nature* (The New Megaphone), and *Eduardo Milán: Poems* (Toad Press). With Kelin Loe, she edits *Spoke Too Soon: A Journal of the Longer.*

EDWARD GAUVIN has received fellowships and residencies from PEN America, the N.E.A., the Fulbright program, the Lannan Foundation, and the French Embassy. His work has won the John Dryden Translation prize and the Science Fiction & Fantasy Translation Award,. Other publications have appeared in the New York *Times, Tin House,* and *Weird Fiction Review.* The translator of more than 150 graphic novels, he is a contributing editor for comics at *Words Without Borders.* He has previously published Thierry Horguelin's work in *Birkensnake* and *Dalkey Archive's Best European Fiction.*

ANN GOLDSTEIN is an editor at *The New Yorker.* In addition to six novels by Elena Ferrante, she has translated works by Pier Paolo Pasolini and Alessandro Baricco. She has received a PEN Renato Poggioli translation award and a Guggenheim Fellowship. She is currently editing the Complete Works of Primo Levi in English.

LYNN GORDON lives in Northern California, where she has worked as a machine operator, a book editor, a chair caner, and a health educator. Her fiction has appeared in *The Southampton Review, Hobart, Zone 3, South Dakota Review,* and elsewhere.

ANDREW GRACE's poems are forthcoming in *The New Yorker,* *Kenyon Review, Missouri Review, Shenandoah, Southwest Review,* and the *Cortland Review* and have recently appeared in *Pleiades, 32 poems,* and *Conduit.* He is the author of three books of poems, most recently *Sancta,* published by Ahsahta Press. He teaches at Kenyon College.

JEFFREY GUSTAVSON is the author of *Nervous Forces* (Alef Books) and two chapbooks from The Frolic Press: *The Ironic Gaze of Señor Ocelot* (2013) and *Chiral Reefs* (2014). His work has appeared in *Grand Street, The New Yorker, Poetry, Fence, Bomb, The Fiddlehead,* and other journals.

HAN DONG was born in 1961 in Nanjing. He and his parents were banished to the countryside during the Cultural Revolution. He studied philosophy at Shandong University and lectured in Xi'an and Nanjing but relinquished teaching in 1993 to write. In the 1980s, he edited the poetry magazine *Tamen* [Them]. He is also an essayist, short-story writer, blogger, and novelist. A collection of his poetry in English can be found in *A Phone Call from Dalian,* from Zephyr Press.

HAIZI (pen name of Zha Haisheng) was born in Anhui province, and wrote avant-garde poetry until his death by suicide in 1989. Since then, his work has been published in innumerable editions across China, making him one of the most celebrated voices of his generation. His work is available in English translation in the collection *Over Autumn Rooftops.*

NICKY HARMAN lives in the U.K. She is a regular contributor of translations to literary magazines. She mentors new translators and judged the Harvill Secker Young Translators Prize in 2012. She was Translator-in-Residence at the Free Word Centre, London, in 2011. She contributes to the literary Web site paper-republic.org and tweets (@cfbcuk) for the China Fiction Book Club.

ALAMGIR HASHMI is author of numerous books of poetry and literary criticism. He has taught as a university professor in Europe, America, and Asia. Recent work appears in *Poetry Review, Poet Lore, New Letters, Poetry International,* and *Connecticut Review.* A Pushcart Prize nominee and a Rockefeller Fellow, he has won many honors and awards for his work, some of which has been translated into European, Asian, and African languages. He is Founding President of The Literature Podium, An Independent Society for Literature and the Arts.

AUDREY HEIJNS is doing her doctoral degree at Leiden University and working as Research Fellow at City University of Hong Kong. She is a translator of Chinese poetry and prose, and editor of the online database Chinese Literature in Dutch Translation.

THIERRY HORGUELIN, born in Montreal in 1965, has lived in Belgium since 1991. For twenty years, he worked as a book reviewer and film critic in Canada, France, and Belgium. He is currently copy-editor-in-chief at Indications (Brussels), editor and book designer for les Éditions Le Cormier (Brussels), and assistant manager of Espace Livres & Création, a Belgian small-press network. Publications include: *Le Voyageur de la nuit* (L'Oie de Cravan, 2005), *La Nuit sans fin* (L'Oie de Cravan, 2009), and *Choses vues* (L'Oie de Cravan, 2012). *La Nuit sans fin* received the Franz de Wever Book Award in 2009. Blog: locus-solus-fr.net.

LORI HORVITZ' poetry, fiction, and creative nonfiction have appeared in a variety of journals and anthologies, including *South Dakota Review, Southeast Review, Hotel Amerika,* and *Quarter After Eight.* Her collection of personal essays, *The Girls of Usually,* is forthcoming from Truman State University Press. Professor of Literature and Language at UNC Asheville, Horvitz also directs the Women, Gender and Sexuality Studies Program.

HSIA YÜ is the author and designer of six volumes of groundbreaking verse, most recently *Poems, Sixty of Them* (2011). She lives in Taipei, where she co-edits the avant-garde journal and poetry initiative *Xianzai Shi* [Poetry Now].

HUANG LIHAI was born in Xuwen and now lives in Guangzhou. He read literature in Sun Yat-sen University and Peking University. He is editor of the poetry magazine *Poetry & People.* He has published a number of books of poems, including *I Know Little About Life* and *The Passionate Mazurka,* and won the 8th Lu Xun Literary Award (Guangzhou, 2009) and Lebanon International Literary Award (2013).

AMORAK HUEY, a former newspaper editor and reporter, teaches writing at Grand Valley State University, in Michigan. His collection *Ha Ha Ha Thump* is forthcoming in 2015 from Sundress Publications. His poems appear in *The Best American Poetry 2012, The Cincinnati Review, The Collagist, Poet Lore, Rattle,* and other journals. Follow him on Twitter: @amorak.

IZAAC JENKS writes stories set in rural and wilderness locales. He spends most of his time on the Pacific coast and in the Rocky Mountains.

NICK KALDIS, Associate Professor of Chinese Studies, is Director of Graduate Studies and Program Coordinator for Chinese Studies in the Department of Asian & Asian American Studies at Binghamton University (SUNY). He is the author of *The Chinese Prose Poem: A Study of Lu Xun's Wild Grass (Yecao)* (Cambria Press, 2014).

KIT KELEN is an Australian poet based in Macao. His poetry has been published in Chinese, Portuguese, Italian, Swedish, and Filipino languages.

ANDREW LADD's début novel, *What Ends*, won the A.W.P. Prize in the Novel. His shorter work has appeared in *Apalachee Review, CICADA, Graze, Memoir Journal, Yemassee,* and *The Rumpus,* among others places. He grew up in Edinburgh, and has since lived in Boston, Montreal, and New York; currently, he lives in London with his wife.

JENNA LE is the author of *Six Rivers* (NYQ Books, 2011), which was a Small Press Poetry Bestseller. Her poetry, fiction, essays, book criticism, and translations have appeared or are forthcoming in *Barrow Street, Bellevue Literary Review, Massachusetts Review, Measure, Pleiades,* and *32 Poems.* She was born in Minnesota and works as a physician in New York.

LIU WAITONG (1975) is a Chinese poet and photographer, who moved to Hong Kong in 1997. Since his debut in 1995, Liu has published many collections of poetry, including *Heiyu Jiangzhi* [Black Rain Will Fall] (2008) and *Yeman Yege* [Barbarous Night Song] (2011). Besides poetry, Liu also writes essays and fiction. He has been awarded several literary prizes in Hong Kong and Taiwan, including the China Times Literary Award and the United Daily News Award. A collection of his poems in English translation, *Wandering in Hong Kong with Spirits,* is forthcoming from Zephyr Press.

CHRISTOPHER LUPKE (Ph.D., Cornell University) is Professor of Chinese at Washington State University, where he is coordinator of Asian languages. He has published edited volumes on the notion of *ming* (command, allotment, fate) in Chinese culture and on contemporary Chinese poetry, and his book on the Taiwanese filmmaker Hou Hsiao-hsien is forthcoming from Cambria Press.

ALEXANDER MAKSIK is the author of the novels *You Deserve Nothing* (Europa Editions) and *A Marker to Measure Drift* (Knopf).

COURTNEY MANDRYK holds M.F.A.s in poetry (University of Michigan) and visual art (Cranbrook Academy of Art). Her writing has appeared in journals such as the *Adirondack Review, DIAGRAM,* and the *Michigan Quarterly Review.* She lives in Charlottesville, Virginia.

LYNN MELNICK is author of *If I Should Say I Have Hope* (YesYes Books, 2012) and co-editor, with Brett Fletcher Lauer, of *Please Excuse This Poem: 100 New Poets for the Next Generation* (Viking, 2015). She teaches at 92Y in N.Y.C. and is the social media and outreach director for VIDA: Women in Literary Arts.

FAYE MOORHOUSE is an illustrator who lives and works in Brighton, U.K. She writes and illustrates dark, disturbing, and beautiful stories. She was awarded the Best New Blood award at D&AD New Blood 2011 and was shortlisted for the Comica Cape Graphic Short Story Prize 2011 for her eighty-page black-and-white graphic novel *The Cat Ladies of Czechoslovakia.* Her work has been published in the New York *Times.*

MU CAO was born in Henan province, China, in 1974. He has no diplomas, is not a member of the Chinese Writers Association, and publishes almost entirely outside of official channels. He has been described as a "folk poet" and a "voice from the bottom of society." His avant-garde novels, poetry collections, and short-story collections include *Outcast, The Transsexual Age, A Treasured Book of Sunflowers, Selected Poems of Mu Cao,* and *Scream of a Hundred Lan Yus.* He lives in Jiangsu province.

SCOTT E. MYERS is a Ph.D. student in the Department of East Asian Languages and Civilizations at the University of Chicago, where he studies contemporary queer Chinese literature and visual arts. He holds a B.A. in philosophy from Hampshire and a master's in Chinese translation from the Monterey Institute of International Studies. A former organizer with experience in China's workers'-rights movement, his translation of the diary of a retail worker in China appears in the *Walmart in China* (Cornell, 2011). His translation of one of China's earliest gay novels, *Beijing Comrades,* by Bei Tong, is forthcoming from The Feminist Press.

PAUL NEMSER's book *Taurus,* which won the New American Poetry Prize, was published by New American Press in November, 2013. His chapbook *Tales of the Tetragrammaton* was published by Mayapple Press in August, 2014. His poems have appeared widely in journals, including *AGNI, Blackbird, Raritan,* and *Tupelo Quarterly.* He and his wife Rebecca live in Cambridge, Massachusetts, and Harborside, Maine.

CHRISTOPHER PATTON is the author of three books, most recently *Curious Masonry: Three Translations from the Anglo-Saxon* (Gaspereau, 2011). The poems published here are from a recently completed manuscript called "Dumuzi," poems from which have also appeared in *FIELD, Colorado Review, Kenyon Review,* and other journals. He teaches creative writing and literature at Western Washington University and blogs at artofcompost.wordpress.com.

AUSTIN R. PICK was born in North Carolina and has traveled widely while pursuing an interest in contemplative practice and a love of the world's wild places. Austin's writing has appeared in *Tahoma Literary Review, Pleiades, Metazen, Adbusters Magazine,* and elsewhere. He lives in Colorado, and his website is www.FudoMouth.net.

STEPHANIE PIPPIN's poetry has appeared in *Boston Review, AGNI,* and *Michigan Quarterly Review.* Her book, *The Messenger,* won the 2012 Iowa Poetry Prize. She lives in St. Louis, MO.

CURTIS ROGERS received his M.F.A. in poetry from N.Y.U.'s Creative Writing Program. He has pieces appearing or forthcoming in *The Literary Review, Coconut, cream city review, DIAGRAM, Painted Bride Quarterly, The Atlas Review,* and elsewhere. He works and lives in Washington, D.C.

SAI SAI (also known as Xi Xi; b. 1938), the pseudonym of Cheung Yin, is among the first generation of writers to have grown up in Hong Kong and is regarded as one of the territory's most important and prolific authors. She began writing poetry in the late 1950s and has published two poetry volumes, *Stone Chimes* (1982) and *The Collected Poems of Sai Sai* (2005), along with numerous novels and short fiction and essay collections. After winning Taiwan's prestigious United Daily fiction prize in 1983, her fame catapulted throughout Greater China, where she has continued to cultivate an enthusiastic readership.

JOSEPH SALVATORE is the author of the story collection *To Assume A Pleasing Shape.* He is a book review editor at *The Brooklyn Rail* and a frequent contributor to the New York *Times Book Review.* His work has appeared in *The Collagist, New York Tyrant, Open City, Post Road,* and *Salt Hill,* among other places. He is an assistant professor of writing and literature at The New School, where he founded the literary journal *LIT.*

EARLE SEBASTIAN, born in Durban, South Africa, of Zulu/Indian heritage, was educated in London. He is an award-winning filmmaker, music producer, creative director, and event curating. He currently resides in Brooklyn, N.Y.

SANDRA SIMONDS is the author of four books of poetry: *Warsaw Bikini* (Bloof Books, 2008), *Mother Was a Tragic Girl* (Cleveland State University Press, 2012), *The Sonnets* (Bloof Books, 2015), and *Ventura Highway in the Sunshine* (Saturnalia Books, 2015). Her poems have appeared or are forthcoming in *The Best American Poetry Anthology*, *Poetry*, *The American Poetry Review*, *The Believer*, *Fence*, *Black Warrior Review*, *Barrow Street*, *The Columbia Poetry Review*, *Gulf Coast*, *Post Road*, and other places.

SONG ZIJIANG, born in Guangdong China, now works in Hong Kong. He has published two books of poems and more than twenty books of poetry translation. He was poet-in-residence at Bundanon, N.S.W., Australia, in 2010-11, and won the 2013 Nosside International Poetry Prize (Italy).

KAREN STEFANO's short fiction, nominated for a Pushcart Prize, has appeared in *The South Carolina Review*, *Tampa Review*, *Green Mountains Review*, *Lost in Thought*, *Metazen*, *Gloom Cupboard*, *Connotation Press*, and elsewhere. She lives in San Diego with her cat. To learn more about Karen and her writing (not to mention the cat), visit stefanokaren.com.

TAM HIO MAN's publications include a novel in English, *Ah Xun's 5 Destinies*, a bilingual book of poems, *The Green Here Is Pink*, and volumes of poetry translation.

SETH BRADY TUCKER is a poet and fiction writer originally from Lander, Wyoming. His first book (*Mormon Boy*) won the 2011 Elixir Press Editor's Poetry Award and was a finalist for the 2013 Colorado Book Award. His second book (*We Deserve the Gods We Ask For*) won the Gival Press Poetry Prize in 2014. He will be the Tennessee Williams Fiction Scholar at Sewanee this year, and his fiction recently won the Shenandoah Bevel Summers Prize. Seth currently teaches at the Colorado School of Mines, and at the Lighthouse Writers' Workshop in Denver.

RACHEL X. WEISSMAN is writing a memoir of her father, a bohemian artist from a New York City shtetl, who had gender-reassignment surgery in 1978. She wrote a play called "Laugh Red Medusa, Laugh, Laugh!" which was produced in Chicago by Theater Oobleck in the mid-eighties. Her journalism has appeared in the New York *Times*, the *New York Observer, Metropolis, Audubon, OnEarth, Entertainment Weekly*, and the *Phoenicia Times*.

MARTIN WINTER was born 1966 in Austria. He is a poet and translator (Bei Ling, Chen Kohua, Hong Ying, Hung Hung, Li Khinhuann, Liao Yiwu, Liu Zhenyun, Ma Lan, Wu Yinning, Yan Jun, Yi Sha, Zheng Xiaoqiong, etc).

XIAO KAIYU is one of the most distinguished and challenging poets writing in China today. He published his first poems in the late 1980s and was particularly prolific during the 1990s, part of a group of poets who were producing work more dense and difficult than had been seen in China in several decades. He was educated in Chinese medicine and lived for several years in Germany before taking up his current position as Professor of Chinese at Henan University. He maintains a deep interest in avant-garde Chinese art and has written criticism on art as well as curated art shows.

YAO FENG is the pen name of Yao Jingming. He was born in Beijing, and now lives in Macao. Yao has widely published both poems and translations. In 2006, he was awarded the Ordem Militar de Santiago de Espada medal by the President of Portugal. He is also the winner of several poetry awards. ◆